A Light-Hearted Look at Seafaring
and other stories

by Len Holder
Master Mariner

Dedication:

To my wife Ann,
who has heard my stories
many many times

Introduction

The Author

I have had a very interesting life as a mariner, a college lecturer and a training consultant. I have had the support of my wonderful wife Ann and the joy of our five children and eight grandchildren. In one way or another I have been involved in education and training all my life. Even before going to Liverpool where the spice of humour is a tradition in education, I found the people I met, and their ideas fascinating. I cannot tell jokes – I never remember the punch lines, but I hope you will enjoy these observations of life. I hope no one is offended when I point out differences between cultures and attitudes. I am not saying one is better than another, only that the differences are interesting.

Len Holder

1 April 2008

Acknowledgements

The author would like to acknowledge the support of Mr Stephen Bond, Managing Director of Videotel Marine International, who have generously offered to sponsor this book. Also thanks to former colleague at Videotel, Barbara (Steinberg) Sherling who has helped with the editing of the stories.

The proceeds from the sale of this book will be donated to maritime and medical charities.

FOREWORD
Julian Parker OBE FNI

All sailors like a good story. At sea we call them 'yarns'. A yarn of course has another meaning as in thread or filament. The term conjures a sense of weaving together, and it is the skill of the story teller to make the tapestry marvellous, full of colour, with unexpected outcomes and better still if it is spiced with sex and humour.

Once on dry land of course fantasy gives way to normality and a good story is one that is not too long, sharp enough to provide a frisson of suspense with an ending that leaves you satisfied and hopefully chuckling with amusement.

Len Holder and I have shared many a long hour in each other's company. We sailed together to the Far East in the ships of the Blue Funnel Line. Then I was a student when Len was a lecturer and later head of department at John Moores University or Liverpool Polytechnic as it was then.

Some time after that I was appointed Secretary of The Nautical Institute and you can sense my delight when Len was elected President - a leader with a real sense of purpose, an effective communicator and above all a President with a wonderful sense of humour.

Reading this collection of short stories is evocative. I can hear Len talking and enjoy the twists, which of course he recognised in the encounters, which gave rise to them. They go back to his schooldays and fan out in an interconnecting network, which reflect his biographical experiences during a rich and varied life.

Len has many sides to his personality and you can find Len the technical man in the research papers held on library shelves and afloat in the navigational systems which incorporate many of his ideas.

Len the manager is more ethereal, cajoling us to excellence in pursuit of our studies or when taking decisions in Videotel where he chairs the company making specialised training materials used on ships throughout the world.

But here we have Len the humanist. Having read this collection of short stories, I think you will share with me that he must be a nice person to know - and you would be right.

LEN'S STORIES

Introduction
Foreword by Julian Parker OBE FNI

School, Sea Scouting, Sailing and Outward Bound

Harwich

1. The Dog and the Newspaper

I had to watch out for my fingers at a house in Portland Crescent. The moment the newspaper appeared through the letter box, a ferocious little dog hurled itself at the door, snatched the newspaper and a few minutes later appeared panting in the bedroom window above the door. I thought "What a well-trained dog – it takes the paper up to its master and mistress in bed!". This happened every day for three years.

Then one day I arrived at the front gate, the door was open, the dog was in the hallway and as it started to run towards me, I bent down to give it the paper. The lady of the house screamed "Don't give the paper to the dog!" I said "Hang

13

on a minute, for three years that dog has been bringing you the paper in bed". "Oh no it hasn't!! For three years it has torn the paper up on the doormat and then rushed upstairs!" Obviously not as well trained as I thought.

2. Supplying Ammunition to the enemy

When the French ships came in to Harwich to shelter in bad weather and wanted to obtain stores, the local chandlers would not deal with them. If they had done so, no English fishermen would buy anything from them ever again. As school boys sailing in the harbour we were asked if we could obtain stores and row them out under cover of darkness. It gave us a chance to try out our newly acquired French language skills. The skipper of the Madeleine Justine from Dunkerque asked for "Les pommes de terre et le bred". I did not know the French word "bred" until he translated it to "pain". They also requested our High School French Mistress, but thinking about the fierce Miss Downton, we advised against this. In return for the stores they gave us fresh crabs and fish.

Although we could understand the skipper well, we could not understand the crew. He said, don't worry, I cannot understand them either, they are from Brittany.

3. Steam Gives Way to Sail

We explored the Rivers Stour and Orwell, and went out into the open sea across Dovercourt Bay to Walton Backwaters. When Harwich and Dovercourt Sailing Club held evening races in the Harbour, we entered. The races started off the Ha'penny Pier at Harwich, sailing a triangular course, round the Guard Buoy, across the channel to the Shotley Spit Buoy, and then back to the Pier.

The Osprey

With our single small sail, we were well behind the rest of the fleet as we started to cross the main channel, and we realised that we had a problem. The Hook of Holland to Harwich passenger steamer "Prinses Beatrix" was going to meet us right in the centre of the channel. Danny was keen not to lose more ground in the race, and he was the one who knew the international Rule of the Road at Sea. "The Rules say 'steam gives way to sail'" he assured me. "We must keep our course and speed!" Adding "Anyway, we are racing, and there are special rules for that!" We kept our nerve, and our course.

There was no way the "Beatrix" could get round us and proceed to its berth at Parkeston Quay, so it veered off to starboard up the River Orwell, where it had to drop anchor to swing on the flood tide, then weigh anchor and proceed back into the harbour before turning hard to starboard and completing its passage very late, thereby disrupting the Boat Trains and upsetting all the passengers.

Not long after that the International Maritime Consultative Organization added a special new section to the Regulations about small craft impeding the passage of larger vessels.....

4. The Spinnaker

Moving from the all-boys Collyer's Grammar School in Horsham to the mixed third form at Harwich County High School was a culture shock, but had some compensations. Danny Goswell was in my class and he taught me to sail. A local business man, Donald Cann, had a 12-foot sailing dinghy which he offered to lend us for the season, if we scraped and painted it. We scraped it, painted it green, sealed cracks in the bottom with a bucketful of tar from the Gasworks, christened it "Osprey", and we were away!

Osprey had a single lug sail and was not very fast. So Danny got hold of a huge section of silk parachute and decided we would use it as a spinnaker. It was evening at Harwich and Dovercourt Sailing Club, and blowing a near-gale off the land, straight down the creek, along which all the club's boats were moored. Danny was in command at the tiller and controlling the mainsail, and I was the spinnaker handler. We went down the creek like a scalded cat, almost out of control, but very exhilarating, weaving from side to side, gybing and resetting the sails. Later we learned that all the Club members, who had wisely decided to stay ashore and a have a beer, had lined the quay to laugh at our erratic progress. The chap who told us, said that each Club Member in turn, as we approached and nearly collided with THEIR boat, changed their attitude to "That is not funny! Totally irresponsible!" Then, when the danger was passed, started laughing again.

5. The Gun

Guns are not a normal part of scouting equipment, but one of our number, Tony Clark, got permission to take his shotgun on an expedition with fellow member Robin Peacock. Not wishing to exert themselves too much, they found in the Scouting Regulations that part of the expedition could be carried out by boat. Neither Tony

Venturer

nor Robin had a "Charge Certificate" to allow them to take charge of the 16-foot Scout Boat "Venturer", so I volunteered to take them from Harwich to Brantham and back (saving them about 16 miles of foot slogging).

As we sailed past Wrabness, Tony decided to inspect and clean the gun. He stood up in the boat, facing aft with the gun tucked under his arm. The barrel was pointing straight at Robin in the bow, who protested that he did not feel safe. Tony swung round to reassure him "Don't worry, it can't fire, the Safety Catch is o ...." At which point there was a loud bang, a splash and a plume of water leapt up alongside the boat. Robin was shocked and not very pleased. He did not know much about guns.

I made the mistake of anchoring the boat in a very steep-sided creek at Brantham. The tide went out as I slept, the keel stuck high on the bank and the boat almost capsized, but I survived. Tony and Robin were very late back for our rendezvous and not speaking to one another when they arrived. The reason emerged later. Well into the return trip, Tony had glanced over his shoulder and noticed the barrel of the gun was not where he expected to see it. "Damn!" He said, "I knew the barrel was loose, I've lost it. We will have to retrace our steps". Mile after mile they searched the undergrowth to no avail. Eventually Robin said "What exactly are we looking for?" "The barrel of the gun!" said Tony. "You don't mean this, do you?" said Robin, raising the barrel of the gun into Tony's line of sight. It had not fallen off at all, just folded down out of sight.

Their relationship was strained for a while after that, but eventually they saw the funny side. Sadly neither is still with us. Both were good companions and a pleasure to know.

6. The Crisp Factory

Just after World War II, there were very few "snack" foods available in kiosks and bars around the country. The East Anglia Potato Crisp Company was doing well with its only real rival, apart from ice cream, being a marshmallow sweet in an ice cream cone. The factory needed extra staff in the run up to Christmas. As a sixth former, aged 16, I needed more pocket money. I volunteered.

My first job was putting the packets into cardboard boxes for despatch, but I soon got onto the production line. I stood with a big tank of glue in front of me. I set a tap to drip glue onto a steel wheel. The unsealed crisp packets came down a chute and I had to pick them up, hold the top against the glue wheel, fold them over, and then put them through heated cog wheels to seal the packet and put the neat "crinkly bit" on the top of the packets. If the glue tap was not set just right, either the packets were not sealed properly or glue flew all over the place. I became very sticky and my fingernails finished up crinkled like the packets. I have never known clocks move so slowly!

Taking an interest in my surroundings, I saw a large complicated machine lying "dead" in the corner. "What does that do?" I asked. I was told it did all the jobs we were doing, putting the crisps and salt in the bags, gluing them, folding them and sealing them. "Why don't you use it?" The answer "It is not accurate enough. The girls can judge the weight of a bag down to the weight of half a crisp. The machine was not accurate –it had to be set overweight to avoid us being caught by trading standards, so it wasted a lot of money. The girls held a stack of empty packets in their right hands and skilfully blew a sharp puff of air (hygiene?) so that the top one opened, they filled it, weighed it and sent it to me in double quick time. So much for automation.

Exploring the factory further, I was shown the machine in which a sharp blade flew round and cut the thin slices of potato. The potato should have been pushed by a metal plunger, but the plunger stopped short of the blade and wasted about three slices of every potato. The managers objected to the waste, and so the last bit was done with your thumb. They also got annoyed when the "crisping fluid" into which the slices fell, took on a reddish hue with blood and had to be changed. You could tell the workers who had worked on that job, they tended to have shorter thumbs than the rest of us.

Valuable experience! I had learned that I did not want to work in a factory ever again! I was not too keen on crisps for a long time after that, either!

7. "My bruvver is a right waster"

Before going to sea with Alfred Holt and Company all future midshipmen were sent on a "toughening up course" at the Outward Bound Sea School in Aberdovey. Lawrence Holt, the "grand old man" of Holt's, was a friend of Kurt Hahn who founded Gordonstoun and other tough schools. I went to Aberdovey in January 1953 - a memorable month which saw terrible storms, the ferry "Princess Victoria" sinking in the Irish Sea and the East Coast floods.

The social mix was very wide, from ex-public school boys from good families, to industrial apprentices from the Midlands and young stewards and deck boys from poor areas of Liverpool, plus everyone in between. I found the language quite difficult, hearing rich "scouse" and "brummie" for the first time. On my course, the authorities sent some boys from Borstal, who had been in trouble with the police, to see if mixing with boys from "normal" homes would change their approach to life.

As a former grammar school boy and Sea Scout, I was chosen as Deputy Watch Leader and asked to take care of a young cockney lad who had spent most of his time in children's homes or wandering the streets and getting into trouble. His name was Wells. I learned a lot from him.

On the day of the gales we were on our major 32 mile expedition over the 3,000ft mountain, Cader Idris. Wells and I walked together and talked all the way. As we started to climb, he said "I can't see the point of climbing up mountains, when you get to the top you just have to climb down the other side. Do you think anyone would notice if we nipped round it instead?" We went over the top and nearly got blown away.

He told me about his family, his mother sad and abused and his father feckless. He said "My bruvver is a right waster. He'll go out of a night, nick three or four wallets, get 40 or 50 quid, and then go and blow it all down at the boozer or betting on the dogs." With great feeling he added "I cannot understand people like that! No sense of responsibility!

Now, if I go out and nick three or four wallets and get 40 or 50 quid, I put it in the Building Society!"

Wells was a good trumpeter and wanted to join the Royal Marines Band. I hope he made it!

Serving at Sea

8. Making Mistakes

When I joined Blue Funnel, I was told that if I made a new mistake, no-one would blame me for it, it would add to the Company's store of knowledge and experience, and be written up as a guide to others. If however, I made a mistake that someone else had made before me, I would be given the "sack". Someone later added facetiously "I understand that if you make THREE new mistakes, they make you a Marine Superintendent or Manager".

ss Helenus Outward Bound

I always tell this story in my lectures to the graduates from the World Maritime University in Sweden, in the week before they go home to about 40 different countries to take up their careers in management, training and administration, or to continue at sea. I urge them not to repeat the mistakes others have already made.

This year one of the graduates came up to me after the lecture and asked for my business card. His remark was enlightening "Wow! Company CHAIRMAN! You must have made a LOT of new mistakes!"

There is no answer to that.

9. Sssshh....Don't Wake the Night Man

The other three midshipmen on my first voyage were "old hands" in their second, third and fourth years. None of us was well paid – I was on £7-10s a month, the others on a few pounds more. They knew that you needed a bit of spare money if you wanted to make the most of nearly six weeks on the Australian Coast, so as soon as we sailed and the inspections had been done, the Half Deck was transformed into a shady poker den. Most of the stewards, deck boys and junior ordinary seamen who came in, left penniless or having signed IOUs to be redeemed on the coast. Whether the middies played fair or not, I cannot judge, but they seldom lost. Even so the "hoard" was not very large and needed to be invested. Each time there was an issue of cigarettes we all bought as many as we could – very few were smoked – it would have been like smoking pound notes.

As we approached Fremantle in Western Australia, I was on duty cleaning the Half Deck. I was told to prepare the cabin for the night man to sleep. The "night man" was shaped like a body and placed in the bottom inside bunk. It was made up of cigarette packets, covered with a counterpane, and hidden behind closed curtains. When the Customs Man knocked loudly on the door, I was instructed to whisper "Sssshh....please try not to wake the night man", show him the dayroom, then tiptoe past the "night man's" bunk into the other sleeping compartment and out again. This was duly accomplished.

The cigarettes sold well to the Wharfies and there was plenty of money to enjoy our stays both ways in Fremantle, Adelaide, Melbourne and Sydney and one stay in Brisbane. If I had been caught, I might have joined the colony's famous criminal fraternity.

10. A New Deck Boy

Docks are dirty, noisy places and it is always good to get to sea into sea breezes and wash the ship clean. We had been in Birkenhead for a week and were now clear of the Scillies on our way to the Far East.

I was on the morning 4 to 8 watch with the First Mate. At 6 a.m. the Bosun appeared to discuss the maintenance daywork with the Mate.

"Good morning, Bosun, time to get started, a lot to do this trip"

"Having the extra Deck Boy will help"

"We haven't got an extra Deck Boy"

The Bosun insisted that there were three boys in the Deck Boys' cabin instead of the usual two. The Mate said, "You are wrong! It must be a Junior Ordinary Seaman who did not get on with his cabin mate, and has moved into the Deck Boys' cabin"

The only way to find out was to have a "roll call". The first two Deck Boys had signed on properly. The third, embarrassed, said "My name is Hhhhi...ram Dddddriver"., He was a stowaway.

Hiram Driver had always wanted to go to sea. He had "run away" to sea at an earlier age and got a criminal record, so now he was banned. He had lived on board our ship for several days before we sailed, and when the other Deck Boys said "Are you coming to the Mercantile Marine Office to sign on?" He said, "I have already been!" Once at sea, he turned to, and worked with the rest – a perfect disguise.

We put a lifeboat down in the Straits of Gibraltar and took him across to join a homeward bound Blue Funnel ship.

Later, a judge commenting on the saga of Hiram Driver said "This lad wanted to go to sea and it is very unfair that he is not allowed to do so." He then added "The jails of the UK are probably full of criminals who would make good merchant seamen, but are banned from seafaring!" Those trying to encourage seafaring as a reputable career were not enchanted by his remark.

11. Emergency Stop

TROILUS was a "Liberty" ship built in 1943 by Bethlehem Fairfield Shipyard at Maryland, USA with a tonnage of 7287grt, a length of 441ft 7in, a beam of 57ft and a service speed of 11 knots. She was launched as the Martha C. Thomas for the War Shipping Administration and transferred to the British Ministry of War Transport, with Alfred Holts as managers, under the 'lease lend' scheme as the Samharle. She was bought for the Ocean Steam Ship Co. and renamed Troilus in 1947. After eleven years service she was sold to Compania Naviera San Augustin S. A. of Panama but registered in Liberia for crewing purposes as the Green River. She was finally broken up at Osaka in 1963.

ss Troilus

Whilst in the Indian Ocean heading east for Malaya, we received a reminder from Liverpool saying that another Blue Funnel Liberty ship *Samwater*, had caught fire homeward bound, off Finisterre, and been abandoned. She could not be stopped, and the attempt to launch her boats resulted in a loss of life. The ships should be capable of stopping using an emergency engine control position outside the engineroom. All Blue Funnel Liberty ships were instructed to conduct an emergency stop drill using the external controls on the Boat Deck. We midshipmen were told to report at 1400 hrs to assist and run messages. The ship would not stop. At 1600 hrs we were still going at full speed.

At 1700 hrs we finished work and went to get showered and changed for dinner. Our bathroom was just below the Boat Deck and our makeshift clothes line was attached to a spindle which passed down into the Engineroom. We found our washing line (and our underwear) was wrapped tightly round the spindle. We unwrapped it but were not brave enough to tell the Master, Mate and Chief Engineer, who were wracking their brains about the problem.

The emergency stopping exercise was repeated the next afternoon and worked perfectly. The senior officers were amazed.

12. The Pet Monkey

The Musi River is over 300 miles long and winds its way through the jungles of Sumatra. To reach the Shell oil refinery at Pladju our ship had to cross the sand bar and follow the twisting channel, at times almost brushing against the trees. Whilst at the refinery delivering equipment and drums of oil, some of the local children came alongside in canoes and offered to sell us fruit. They also had a very small monkey, which the deck boys bought as a pet.

Everyone loved the monkey, which was very friendly and happy and played with everyone – except one person. For some reason, it hated "Chippy" (the ship's carpenter), and whenever he went near, it bared its teeth and backed away, hissing.

28

The ship's next port of call (well not really a port) was the Rejang River in Borneo. We arrived on Saturday morning and the agent arrived in his hollowed out log canoe with its big Johnson outboard motor. He brought some mail and told us we would start loading logs on Monday. At "smoko" (the morning tea break) everyone gathered round Number 4 hatch and the centre of attraction was the monkey. It was jumping from the deck to the hatch, then going up to people for pieces of banana, having a great time. While it was standing on the ship's rail, the carpenter went up to it, and in a moment it had jumped backwards into the fast-flowing river and disappeared. Everyone was really angry with "Chippy" – he knew the monkey was frightened of him, and he should have known better than to approach it. Chippy was ostracised all Saturday, all Sunday, and at breakfast on Monday.

At about 8.30 on Monday, with the hatches open and the derricks rigged ready to load, the agent arrived with the paperwork and went to the Mate's Office. After discussing the cargo he said "By the way, do you realise you have a monkey standing on the top of your rudder?" The Mate was surprised and organised a lifeboat to rescue the monkey and bring it back on board. As the ship was light, the top of the rudder was just out of the water, and the monkey had swum across and climbed onto it. It was very cold and hungry, but was soon fed and well looked after. Even so, Chippy did not have many friends for the rest of the voyage!

13. Krakatoa

The "Phemius" was homeward bound from Djakarta in Java and was going to call at Padang in Western Sumatra. This meant going through the Sunda Strait, with its volcanic islands and strong currents.

mv Phemius

I was on watch as we entered the Strait. Captain Macmillan came on the bridge and asked, "Have you ever seen Krakatoa?" I said I hadn't. He said he had never seen it really close to, and suggested we go to have a look. "We are in good time for a dawn arrival in Padang – we have time to spare. Starboard Easy!" Krakatoa is famous for the huge volcanic explosion which blew away half of the island on 27th August 1883 and affected the whole world. We sailed in close to the face of the remaining half of the island. It was very interesting to see how nature re-colonises after catastrophic events. Since 1883 several new (and thus uncharted) islands have emerged nearby. Lucky we did not hit any of them!

When we got back onto our course line Captain Macmillan said "Rub out the position fixes on the chart, and put new ones on our proper course line. Make a note in the logbook that we have had severe adverse currents!"

14. Palmer

When I joined the British Rail Container ships on the Harwich – Antwerp run, the shipboard discussion was more about home, gardens and cars than the stories of the Far East and Australia that I was used to in Blue Funnel.

Whether it was on the "Isle of Ely" or the "Colchester" everyone I met was sad about someone called Palmer. They talked about him with great feeling. "Sad about Palmer!" "Pity about poor old Palmer!" "Palmer was a real gentleman!". "It is not the same without Palmer!" I thought he must have died.

When we had a quiet moment, I asked the Mate "Who was Palmer and what happened to him?" He told me Palmer was formerly an Able Seaman and now was in jail in Ipswich. So I asked "Why?"

Palmer knew that the two container ships loaded thousand of cigarettes in the Forward Strong Room and sometimes they stayed on board for a long time before the ship sailed. Palmer was on leave. With a group of friends, he rowed across the river and went to the dining saloon, took the key of the Mate's door, opened it, got the strongroom key, lowered several boxes of cigarettes into his boat, and rowed back to the Suffolk shore.

31

He was not caught on that occasion. Later, he realised the wages were in the office safe overnight before payday. He was caught on his next cross-river expedition. A security man thought it odd that the repair gang were using an oxy-acetylene burner that late at night!

Why was he missed?

The Mate left his door key hidden under a cushion in the saloon, so that any officer arriving early could get into his cabin. Palmer knew the Mate would get into trouble if he just took the key to rob the strongroom, so before he left the ship, he broke the Mate's door down with a fire axe, so that the Mate would not get into trouble. He was a gentleman and considered his shipmates.

He also made better toast for the watchkeepers at midnight than any other able seaman. He was sorely missed.

15. Enough to make her weep...

I was the first member of the family to visit my Uncle when he was Harbour Master at Port Swettenham, in Malaya. His Chinese cook was very pleased that Captain Hatcher's young nephew was coming on a ship from England and decided to plan a great welcome by cooking a Chinese banquet for me – 32 courses in all, if I remember correctly. I had never

Captain Hatcher.
Harbourmaster

eaten Chinese food before, though I love it now. I was more used to simple English country fare, and not too much of that during World War II. I bravely made it to the 16th course before calling it a day. I learned later that the cook had cried for days afterwards. I felt I had let the side down.

16. Port Swettenham and the Raincoat

The kit list for Midshipmen included three sets of "whites", the tropical uniform. Keeping them white and getting them washed and starched was a problem. One way of turning them into a soggy bundle, was to wear them under a raincoat in a tropical downpour. Leaving Port Swettenham in tropical rain, I decided that no-one would notice if, when on the bridge, I just wore my raincoat and left my precious whites in the cabin.

All went well as we let go and pulled away from the quay and the ship started to turn. The Pilot and the Master wanted to go onto the other bridge wing, but it was inches deep in water. "Middy, just go and clear that scupper!" I jumped to it. I did not want to let the bottom of my raincoat get wet by crouching down, so I bent over to clear it. The water drained away, and nothing more was said.

The next time I visited Port Swettenham, where my Uncle was Harbour Master, I discovered that part of my anatomy had been widely discussed amongst the chattering classes in the town. When I was introduced to people, I noticed nudges, winks and knowing grins!

17. Big Vents on a Glen Boat

In my days at sea, most Blue Funnel ships had Liverpool crews and the associated Glen Line fleet had Hong Kong Chinese crews. We sailed with both. It was a fact that the Liverpool crews liked to do challenging "real" seamanship jobs, like rigging the Jumbo Derrick, but got bored quickly with cleaning and polishing, but the "Glen boats" shone and everything that moved was cleaned and greased. The big cowl ventilators which either sucked air out of, or directed air into, the cargo holds moved much more smoothly on Glen boats. When the "standby man" was sent round to put them back to wind in a shower, it was easy.

Rumour has it – I cannot confirm – that a Chinese seaman on lookout on the focsle head on a cold night stood inside one of the vents and fell asleep, lulled by the warm air which rises from the tropical cargo. He should have been keeping a lookout and ringing one bell for ships or other objects to starboard, two strokes for port and three for something dead ahead.

When it started to rain, the standby man turned the vent to face aft, waking the lookout man, whose first sight was a ship dead ahead (his own) showing green and red sidelights and masthead light very close. He reportedly leap out of the vent, gave three stokes on the bell and jumped over the bow.

Nice story but probably not true, though it might be....

18. New Technology

Not having been formally trained as a teacher, I was surprised to be invited to contribute to a course by Her Majesty's Inspectors of Education, for former ships' officers who were starting a career as technical college lecturers. It was a one week course held at Warsash Maritime Centre. My subject was "the use of new technology in teaching". My message was to warn new teachers about getting so interested in the technology that they would forget the subject matter that they were supposed to be teaching.

I used as an example, the following story.

As a junior officer, I had been to the Purser's Office when the ship was approaching Japan, to post a letter, which I had carefully kept below 10 grams. As I was leaving the office a deck boy came in with a large package to send home, and I warned him: "That looks heavy, postage rates are very high from Japan. It will cost you a fortune"

He replied in a broad scouse accent: "It's worth it, Sir. I hate writing letters, so I bought two tape recorders, one for myself and one for my Mum and I don't have to write letters any more. We send tapes to one another".

I enquired "How long are the tapes?"

"Thirty minutes"

I said: "I couldn't talk for thirty minutes. After two or three minutes I would be going errr..... ummm.........."

"Funny you should say that, because that is exactly what happened to me, so now, I write it all down first!"

The serious message was to choose technology that makes your teaching better than before, not just different.

As I left, I said to the HM Inspector "Was that OK?" He replied: "Mmmm. I am not sure. They enjoyed it, but I am not sure your message came across."

Several years later I was on the phone to a lecturer in another college. He said "I remember you, you gave a lecture on the HMI's course when I started teaching. I remember it very well. He then repeated, almost word for word, the story above. I thought "What do HMI's know? He did remember it!" He then spoiled it all by saying "I think you were trying to get across a serious point at the time, but I can't remember what it was!"

Ever since then I have had a healthy respect for the wisdom of HMIs.

19. The Garden Gate

When my ship called at Penang on the voyage home, I was asked by Uncle Len, the Harbour Master, to bring home to the UK a large mahogany and brass ship's wheel. It had been the wheel of an old buoy tender with rod and chain steering. The tender was being broken up and replaced by a new tender MV Aktina. Uncle Len said "When I retire to a country cottage, I want to have the wheel as the centre-piece of my garden gate."

Leaving the ship in Liverpool, my taxi was stopped at the dock gates and the policeman looked in, to see among my luggage, a large flat brown paper parcel with spokes sticking out. The policeman smiled and said "I think you had better take that back, son, they will be needing it next voyage!"

20. Threatened by Four Stripes

I spent 15 months on M.V. "Machaon" as Third Mate. At the end of each voyage, I longed to get away from the Master Captain H. E. Readshaw and the First Mate Mr D.K. Dunlop. I suppose it was my skill at keeping out of trouble that caused them each time to ask for me to go back next voyage.

Captain Readshaw had had a hard time in World War II and was known to have a drink or three, or perhaps four. When he blew up the voice pipe at ten at night, I think you could have lit the fumes. I never tried that, but the fumes knocked you backwards. Having said that, Captain Readshaw was a superb natural seaman and took us through fishing fleets and bad weather with consummate skill.

Mr Dunlop's main ambition was to become Master of his own ship. On one occasion he had been asked to take over command of an earlier ship for a few days when the Master was ill. I think it was in Singapore. On the strength of that, Mr Dunlop had bought a new uniform with the four stripes and "scrambled egg" on his cap, ready for the next opportunity.

He hated Captain Readshaw and "baited" him by hanging his four-striped uniform just outside Captain Readshaw's door when the weather was fine "Just to give it an airing."

It was the Second Mate who pointed out to me that, unlike other Masters and First Mates who walked round the decks in port to check on the cargo, Captain Readshaw never went round with Mr Dunlop if the hatches were open.

According to the Second Mate "He is afraid of being pushed over the edge, when no-one is looking." With my long association with the two, I think he could well have been right.

21. Picking Up the London Pilot at Brixham

Glen Line ships heading up the English Channel for London normally picked up the London pilot at Brixham, rather than having to join the "crowd" round the busy pilot cutter off Folkestone.

When I was Third Mate, my job was to see that the pilot ladder was properly rigged and the pilot (and his bag) arrived safely on board. As we approached, the Master gave me several cartons of cigarettes and said "These are for the boatmen, pass them down in a bucket, but ONLY IF I GIVE YOU A THUMBS UP SIGN. A Customs man sometimes comes out with the boatmen. It is always the same one and I will recognise him, if he is there, we don't send the cigarettes down!"

As the pilot boat came alongside, I looked up at the bridge, the Master gave the "thumbs up" and I passed the cigarettes down to the boatman. I escorted the pilot up to the bridge. After the usual greetings the Master said "I see you've got a new boatman Pilot!" To which he replied "No, but we do have a new Customs man!" I thought we might be in real trouble. The Master said "That's torn it, I sent cigarettes down to the boatmen, will that get them into trouble".

"No" said the pilot, "but they will be disappointed, because when the Customs man is there, they have to divide them three ways instead of just two".

22. The Cook and the Galley Boy

My first job as a watchkeeping officer was as fifth mate on the 1926-built ship M.V. "Phemius". They told me in the office that the ship did not have five mates, so everyone on board would probably call me "fourth mate" but they had made a special post for me, as I was still in the third year of my four year apprenticeship. The "special" post differed from the normal fourth mate's job only because the wages were £32 a month instead of the normal £35. Even £32 was a great improvement on Midshipmen's wages which started at £7.50 a month in the first year and did not get much above £10 in the later years. I felt very rich.

"Phemius" had no radar and no gyro compass. She had been built to carry pilgrims from the Malay archipelago to Jeddah in the "hadji" season. As junior watchkeeper you had to take part in the ritual at noon when the Master and all the Mates took sextant altitudes of the sun as it crossed the meridian, calculate the latitude and report it to the Master, starting with me, as the most junior. Your professional reputation was very much on the line.

One day in the Java Sea we were all assembled on the port wing of the bridge, when we looked aft and saw the galley boy sprint across the after end of Number 4 hatch at an amazing speed. Shortly afterwards the reason for his haste became clear as the Chief Cook followed him across the hatch at equal speed brandishing a meat cleaver.

The Master looked at all the Mates waiting to take the important noon sun sights and obviously considered my navigational skills were dispensable. "Just go and sort that lot out Fourth Mate" he ordered.

College courses never taught us how to deal with a frenzied Chinese cook, but I decided to stay well clear of the cleaver. Standing at the forward end of Number 3 hatch I yelled with all my might at the two as they rushed past "Hey, that's enough of that. Stop it immediately!" Fortunately the Cook, who was a bit overweight had decided he could not catch the galley boy and was ready to give up. On investigation we discovered that the cheeky galley boy had insulted the Cook's mother and touched a very raw nerve.

23. Are you the Daddy or the Uncle?

As a midshipman, leaving home for a voyage in uniform, as I closed the garden gate a little boy aged about five asked me "Are you the Daddy or the Uncle in that house?" I replied "I am not the Daddy or the Uncle, I suppose I am the little boy!"

Mentioning the conversation when I next came home, my mother explained who the boy was. He lived opposite. His father was a seafarer, and as soon as his daddy went to sea, his mother invited "uncle" to stay until just before daddy returned. It didn't work like that in our house.

24. Finding Great Great Grandfather

My mother told me that my great great grandfather had been master/owner of a four-masted barque, sailing out of Ipswich to ports all over the world. Unfortunately he caught yellow fever in Java and died. Knowing that the Blue Funnel ship on which I was serving as a midshipman, was calling at Surabaya, she suggested that I find his grave there. I hired a trishaw and was pedalled round to every graveyard in Surabaya and could not find any inscription to "Captain William Colthorpe". Returning home, I reported that I had visited every graveyard in Surabaya. My mother said "Did I say Surabaya? It might have been Batavia (Djakarta)!"

My thought was "Yes Mum. And it might not have been Djakarta either" so I stopped looking. Now, fifty years later, having almost retired, I might start looking again.

25. Thick as a Hedge

The English have two problems with language. One is that they are not very good at learning other peoples' languages. The other is that they are not very accurate or clear when using their own.

When I was already a college lecturer, I was coming across from the Hook of Holland to Harwich as a passenger on a misty night. My former shipmates invited me on to the bridge of the "St Edmund" as we approached the outer entrance to the port. The Master called the pilot cutter "Preceder" which was inside the harbour and asked "What is the visibility like where you are?" The reply came back in a very thick Harwich accent "'A's as thick as hedge 'ere boy!"

Some months later in the Hague, at an international conference, I used that incident to explain that you should always use clear Standard Maritime English in communications, especially when you are on "open channel" VHF radio and everyone else can hear.

I explained that "'A's as thick as hedge 'ere boy!" was not standard English and should not be used.

My message clearly confused an Egyptian delegate who sought me out after the lecture. He said "Sir, I did not understand 'hedge buoy'. I understand port hand buoy and starboard hand buoy, but what is a hedge buoy?" My explanation that it was not a buoy, but a form of friendly greeting, added to his confusion. I had learned another lesson – keep to simple examples for multi-cultural audiences.

26. The Hazards of Going Away to Sea

May 2005. It was the day of the reunion for the Blue Funnel Line cadet ships "Calchas" and "Diomed" in Liverpool. I

M.V. Calchas

chatted to the taxi driver going from Lime Street to the Atlantic Tower Hotel. He said "My next door neighbour was in the Merchant Navy. He was a steward on the QE2. One voyage he came home, went in the front door, hung his hat in the hall and went into the living room. He found a strange family in there. His parents had moved while he was away and not told him! He had to stay with us for a week until he found them again. I always thought his father was not a very nice man".

27. The Red Faced Monkey

Blue Funnel ships used to offer a couple of round voyages for Singapore and Malayan cadets from our local associates the Straits Steamship Company. One such cadet was Nelson Miranda, a Singaporean (sadly since killed in a motor accident) whose family were from Kerala in southern India. He had a great gift for languages, and besides speaking English and Malay, was fluent in several Indian and Chinese dialects.

He was on cargo watch with me in Bangkok. We went down No 3 Hold and the stevedores alerted one another and said something in Chinese. I asked Nelson "What did they say?" He replied "They said 'Look out, here comes the red-faced monkey!'" I was angered by their rudeness and told him I wanted to say something equally rude to them in Chinese.

Nelson said "No Sir, you have got it all wrong. They like and respect you!"

Me: "Then why were they so rude?"

Nelson: "They call all white people red-faced monkeys.

If they did not like you they would have said 'Look out! Here comes the red-faced monkey bastard!'"

So that is all right then!

28. Third ship at the Rough Tower

On one of my first passages from Parkeston to Antwerp on the small British Rail container ships "Isle of Ely" and "Colchester", I was on the first watch passing the Cork Lightship, and the Rough Towers. The Master came up on the bridge to see all was OK before going to bed, and conversation wore a bit thin. Remembering my days on the pilot cutter, I said "Do you remember the pile of three wrecks out here, a few years ago, Sir?" It was World War II "E-Boat Alley" where so many ships were sunk, that two landed on top of one another. The third ship in the pile was a modern coaster, which looked as if it was bound for London but never moved. I continued "I wonder who the idiot was who ran the third ship onto the pile!" The Master said "Yes. I wonder! Good night Second Mate, I am going to turn in".

I went into the wheelhouse where the wheelman, who had overheard the conversation, said "You were sailing a bit close to the wind there, Second!" "Was I? Why?" "The old man was with Stephenson Clarke's in the coal trade before joining British Rail. It was him who did it!"

29. The Chicken

The railway ships ran between Harwich and the Hook of Holland almost as if they were on railway lines. It just happened that two Decca Navigator green pattern lines fitted the courses to and from the Galloper lightship and the Maas Buoy off the Hook. If you were on line number 36 and passed the ship going the other way at anything significantly more or less than 8 cables, you would tell him "You are off your line (37)". New ships all had the new Decca Navigator, so that if you had an interruption of the signal you could reset them from scratch using the Lane Identifier. Our Mark 4 Deccas had no Lane Identifier, so were not much more advanced that the system used for the D-Day landings which used gas meters to check how many lanes you had crossed. We had to set it up while still in sight of reliable navigation marks.

One Second Mate left the Maas Buoy and forgot to set the Decca, so ended up "lost" in the North Sea. He knew he would be in trouble if he called the Master, so, reckoning that if he headed west, he must eventually find England, he ploughed on. The next thing he knew, there were waves breaking each side of the ship (a sign that anyone who has been in very shallow water will recognise). A shadowy figure appeared on the bridge wing (the Master woken by the noise), but said nothing. The tide was just high enough on the Galloper Sands for the ship to get across and into deeper water, they fixed the ship's position from the lightship, the Master went below, and the ship proceeded into port.

The Second Mate expected to be reported to the Marine Superintendent, reprimanded, and sacked. On arrival in Harwich, nothing was said. Days went by and they turned into weeks. Still nothing was said.

One day, the Second Mate was going out of the dock gates when the policeman called him over and asked to look in his holdall. He put his hand in and pulled out a chicken. "Allo! Allo! What have we got here?" To which the true reply was "I have not seen it before in my life". The Second Mate was sacked for stealing a chicken. It had been planted in his bag, and the policeman had been alerted.

The moral to this story, is that if the Master had reported the Second Mate for his navigational shortcomings, he would have been sacked as well for not supervising him properly. This way, the Master was not implicated. Hence the warning in the railway ships to anyone thinking of "crossing" his senior officers. "Remember the chicken!"

30. See me in my office at Nine O'clock!

The weather in the winter of 1962 to 1963 was dreadful, fog, ice and snow. This was my time in the railway ships at Harwich. I was relieving Second Mate and so could be sent on any ship, even the "prestige" fast passenger ships on the Harwich-Hook of Holland run.

As Second Mate of the s.s. "Arnhem" I had done the first half of the crossing as Officer of the Watch. We had sailed late, because the Expresses from all over Europe were delayed by ice and snow. The visibility was patchy. Outside the Hook we had to thread our way through the East European fishing fleet. We had kept up as high a speed as we thought safe, so as to try to meet the deadline for the Parkeston Quay to London Boat trains – 18 knots most of the time.

When we arrived at 6 am, I was handed a curt note from the Marine Superintendent, Captain Wright saying "See me in my office at Nine O'clock!"

ss Arnhem

Three hours to wait while my mind dwelt on all the terrible things I might have done. Had I hit a fishing boat without realising it and drowned the crew? Had I damaged thousands of pounds worth of fishing gear? Had I damaged our own ship? Only time would tell. Three hours is a long time.

At 9 am sharp I was outside the Superintendent's office and he called me in. He waved a white envelope in front of me and said "Did you send this?" I recognised the requisition for chart pencils and rubbers I had sent in earlier in the week and said "Yes, Sir!". "This is an INTERNAL memo. Internal memos go into BROWN envelopes". "Sorry Sir, What did you want to see me about?" "I haven't finished with this yet!" "You wrote the address in BALL POINT PEN! Internal memos are addressed in pencil, so they can be rubbed out and used again!". "Sorry Sir, What did you want to see me about?" "I haven't finished with this yet!"

Looking as if he was about to tear out his hair he said with great passion "To crown it all, not content with using a white envelope and writing in pen, YOU STUCK IT DOWN!". "Sorry Sir, What did you want to see me about?"

"That's all! You can go now."

Liverpool and The Wirral

31. Otterspool Promenade

Classroom at Aulis

Moving to Liverpool to take over day to day responsibility for running Alfred Holt and Company's new Training Centre "Aulis" was like suddenly acquiring a family of 110 teenage boys to add to our own three (or more precisely 2.5) children.

The Head of the Midshipmen's Department was Dick Hutson, who lived next door at Dulcie Lodge. I am indebted to him for this story. Dick and his wife Mavis had Cavalier King Charles spaniels and used to walk down to Otterspool Promenade by the River Mersey, to exercise them.

The shady car park near the promenade was a favourite haunt of lovers, getting away from the bright lights and noise of Liverpool and Garston.

Dick tells me that one evening he walked discreetly past a steamed up and gently rocking car and nearly tripped over one of our Engineer Cadets who was lying horizontal next to the car siphoning out petrol into a can. Taken aback, he thought quickly through several possible actions and chose to walk on looking straight ahead.

32. Laundry

Many wives who have seafarer husbands are grateful that they have been "housetrained" and know how to wash and iron their own clothes. Some rather spoiled children who came to sea found this chore beneath them and I sailed with one midshipman who arrived with a stack of about 10 sets of underwear, which he placed in his wardrobe. At the end of the week when we did our washing, he declined. He simply placed the dirty ones at the bottom of the stack and took the next clean pair off the top. By the time we got to Singapore he was not very nice to know. Come to think of it, his initials were J M B-O (hyphenated). The B.O. part was probably appropriate.

When I was at the Blue Funnel Line Training Centre, one mother of a boy joining new from school said "I see there are washing machines and ironing boards. Who teaches them to wash and iron?". To which I replied politely "I am afraid you do Madam, before he arrives!". I even saw a mother tying the shoe laces of a young man, buying his first uniform at the Naval Outfitters before starting his first voyage.

Once, at "Aulis", a terrified cleaner ran into my office and said she had just been buried – under a mountain of filthy clothes. An Engineer Cadet from a well-to-do family who had studied at a good Public Boarding School had been taking clean clothes out of his drawers and piling them into his wardrobe when they were dirty. Eventually the hinges and the door catch gave way and the cleaner was right in the path of the avalanche.

The same Engineer Cadet went home at Christmas and was the cause of a very nasty letter from his father to me, along the lines "My son has come home with filthy underwear, and as he has been living with you for three months and no-one complained I assume you all have dirty underwear…" I drafted a reply which said "Since he lived with you and your wife for 16 years before joining us, I assume you and your wife etc etc". I showed it to the Head of Department who would not let me send it. He sent a more diplomatic reply.

33. Pensby Conservatives

When we moved to the Wirral Ann and I wanted to become part of the local community and we looked at several organisations. The churchgoers seemed to be too busy praying to do much for their fellow citizens. The Liberal Party talked a lot but was " all over the place". The Labour Party hardly existed in the old Wirral constituency (19 Conservatives and one Liberal on the Wirral Council?). We joined the Conservatives who were the ones that were working the hardest for the community. Our first mistake was to be introduced to everyone at a "Tramps and Tarts" dance. When we met people in the village next day, we did not recognise anyone. We soon found plenty of needy people around—a blind widow with two young children, very old people who refused to accept charity etc—all within a few hundred yards of our home.

34. Canvassing: brushes with the opposition

When it came to the May elections we all took part in house to house canvassing, inviting the residents to vote for our candidate. I went to a house in Highfield Drive. The front garden was immaculate. There were no weeds in sight and every tulip and daffodil stood to attention without a petal out of place. The house was smartly painted too, but had a leaky gutter, and as I stepped back to avoid the drip the door opened and I caught my heel on the kerb at the edge of the drive and fell backwards into the tulips. Rather than struggle to my feet, I delivered my election address from the flowerbed. They refused to vote for our man. I learned later that they were died-in-the wool Liberals anyway!

I had another interesting but unrewarding experience in Penmon Drive. Instead of closing the door quickly, an attractive blonde lady said that she would like to hear my views on a number of political issues, so would I like to come in and have a cup of tea. After about twenty five minutes of interesting conversation I got back to my task. When I returned to Conservative Headquarters I proudly announced that I thought I had persuaded the lady to vote for us. The old hands said "No way! she was just keeping you off the street. Her husband is the Labour candidate!"

35. The Coffee shop in Heswall

Having taken early retirement from the Polytechnic, I became an independent consultant. I worked from home and used Ad Hoc, a fax and photocopying agency in Heswall. At about coffee time most mornings we would walk to Heswall, Ann would do some shopping and I would go to Ad Hoc for copying and faxes. We would then go into Gerrards Coffee shop in Castle Buildings for coffee, and to check appointments in our diaries. After we had done this for a while we met another regular Justin Routledge (cousin of Patricia Routledge - Mrs Bucket of TV fame).He said that we had intrigued the other regulars. We obviously were not married because we didn't argue enough. The fact that we compared diaries must mean that we were illicit lovers (probably a boss and his secretary) arranging times and places for our assignations. They were quite disappointed to find that we had been married for nearly forty years!

36. Driving Lessons

Ann had a brain tumour operation in 1987. She was told by the Consultant that two years after the operation she would be able to drive a car. Our sons were amazed, "That's wonderful Mum because you couldn't drive before".

Teaching your loved ones to drive is never easy. After a few lessons in her Dad's little automatic Standard 8 Ann was doing quite well. The clutch on our sit-up-and-beg pre-war Ford Anglia was fierce and she didn't find it easy. Ann would not pull out to drive round a stationary car, and we had to change seats for me to drive round it. We were not getting anywhere other than nearer to a divorce, so we suspended driving lessons.

Later, Tony Rawson one of the lecturers at Riversdale College had told us that he had found an old disused airfield in Lancashire to let his wife get a "feel" of their car before venturing into traffic, so we had another go. We found the airfield and Ann took over the driving while I played games with the children in the back. I had noticed that the whole airfield was clear, except for one small pile of bricks at the side of the runway. Suddenly there was an enormous crunching sound from the back of the car as we hit the pile of bricks. Ann's explanation " Well it's no good just driving round and round, I need to practice reversing round a corner, and the bricks were the only corner I could see".

I reported to Tony that it had not been 100% successful. He said "Neither was ours. At one point my wife said "What do I do now, there is an aeroplane in my rear view mirror!"

37. Have you paid and displayed?

For many years we had taken our children to West Kirby swimming pool and parked in the free car park at the back, so when the grandchildren were visiting we took them. We parked the car and went into the pool. When we came out there was a parking ticket on my car - a £40 fine for not paying and displaying. I had failed to notice the new signs in large letters about the parking no longer being free.

I decided to appeal and told a sob story in my letter, saying that I was old and couldn't see very well, and I had left my glasses at home. It really was such a sorry tale that I might have been banned from driving because of poor eyesight. However they let me off, but added that they had made a note of my car registration number and if I tried that one again I would not get off! Shortly afterwards we sold the car.

38. You don't recognise me

Ann and I were returning from the theatre in Liverpool on the Merseyrail Underground to Birkenhead. I saw a familiar mature and bearded face opposite, who leaned forward and said:

"You don't recognise me, do you!"

Me: "Yes I do"

"No you don't!"

Me: "Yes I do. You are our milkman, Express Dairies. You deliver our milk every morning!"

"Correct! But you don't recognise me. When you were Fourth Mate in Blue Funnel, I was a Junior Midshipman, and we did a voyage together on the 'Glenearn' to Japan."

He was quite right. I had not recognised him as a former shipmate. I think it was the beard.

A postscript to this story is that when T & J Harrison's were short of good junior officers, they invited former mariners to do a refresher course and go back to sea. He went. He was a very good officer. His Superintendent was singing his praises. I pointed out that his gain of a good third mate was our loss of a very good milkman.

39. A Very Conscientious Milkman

Same milkman. Express Dairies brought out a new "line" of yoghurts and our milkman's sales technique was forceful: "Look. I'm desperate! I've got to get rid of these yoghurts! Someone is going to have the 'trots' tonight, it might just as well be you!"

Ann was pregnant at the time.

Ann was very embarrassed a few months later, when in the middle of the village shops amongst friends and neighbours with the new baby in her pram, the Express Dairy milk float was speeding past, screeched to a halt, and the milkman, in his uniform, rushed across the road and said (sticking his head into the pram). "Let me see, what did you have then?" Everyone was surprised, including Ann, and the neighbours wondered…..

39. Perceptions

The Honourable Company of Master Mariners holds its North West Outport quarterly lunches in the Athenaeum, which is a gentlemen's club, founded in 1797 to provide a meeting place where ideas and information could be exchanged in pleasant surroundings. The Athenaeum has a distinguished membership of proprietors drawn from every walk of life across the city of Liverpool and the North West of England. Early proprietors took a major part in the national movement to end slavery. Past proprietors have included Nobel Laureates. Today the proprietorship is drawn among others from those engaged in commerce, the church, the law, the city's large academic community, public service and the armed forces.

Put more simply by the taxi driver when we arrived at Lime Street Station and asked for "The Athenaeum, please". He asked "Dat's the millionaires' club - are you's two millionaires, or what?"

40. Liverpool Limits

Having put on a smart suit to go to dinner in London, I was not best pleased to stand on a wobbly paving stone near Milton Keynes station and get a jet of muddy water up my right trouser leg, which filled my shoe.

Things improved when we realised that the train we had joined came from Liverpool. We sat opposite an Everton supporter and his wife, and started chatting about Liverpool and its people.

"You've got to be very careful what you say these days", he said. You can't joke on the buses any more. He said "When I was younger, I always used to say to the driver or conductor 'Is this bus OK for Gretna Green, Mate' and he would reply with something snappy like 'Yes, you're OK on this one, but you'll need to change at Old Swan'. Nowadays, if you said "Is this bus OK for Gretna Green", they would look worried, stare at you, and think a madman had got on their bus.

We discussed where Liverpool humour stops geographically and decided it was in the Lancashire hills somewhere near Chorley. He said he and his mate had stopped at a hilltop café near Chorley, parked the car and gone in. In his usual cheery way he had said to the girl behind the counter "Two coffees and bucket of water for the horse, please, love". A few moments later she came out with the bucket of water and they had to explain that they hadn't really got a horse. It was something called "a joke". To which the girl said "Oh, I see. But you know, we get a lot of horses through here".

41. The Extra Masters Class

Studying for Extra Masters, we got bored with ship construction in the classroom and wanted to go and see ships being built at Cammell Laird shipyard in Birkenhead. The shipyard managers were very pleasant, but said "Sorry. We are building submarines for the Royal Navy. The work is highly classified and so you cannot visit the yard! Call us in a few months, you may be able to come!"

About two months later:

"Can we come yet?"

The manager "You've already been, why do you want to come again?"

Me: "We have not been!"

Him: "Yes you have, about two months ago. I showed you round!"

Me: "I am sorry, but you are mistaken. We have not been!"

Pause for thought.

Him: "I think I know what must have happened. Last time you asked if you could visit, we also had a request from a party of Chinese Communists. I remember now thinking how strange it was that all the Extra Masters Class from the college were Chinese! That explains it." So much for security!

We did eventually visit and found it very interesting.

42. Becoming a Teenager Again

About 6 pm recently my meal was interrupted by a smartly dressed salesman trying to sell me the Carphone Warehouse Talktalk phone service. Knowing that British Telecom had been overcharging for years, I was interested.

When it came to my personal details,

He asked: "Are you over 18?"

I replied "Yes, by quite a long way"

Him "You're not over 70 are you?"

Me "No, I am 69"

Him "Oh dear, I cannot sign up anyone under 18 or over 70"

Me "I am not over 70, I am 69"

Him: "But you are nearly 70 and I need to phone my boss to see if I have to get a counter-signature. Do you have anyone in the house who could countersign?"

Me: "Yes, my wife, but she is 69 as well"

Him "Oh dear, I really must phone my boss"

I had not realised that, at the age of 70, we will be re-entering teenage years of being irresponsible and needing supervision.

It is quite an exciting prospect.

43. Will the last man out....

Ann and I were watching the RAF Falcon Parachute team land on the beach at Clacton on a very windy day. All eight men landed close to the crosses marked on the sand – very impressive.

A boy of about six standing near us with his mother was thrilled by the spectacle, but suddenly a frightened look appeared on his face as he looked up at the plane, which was disappearing into the distance.

In a worried voice: "Mum, if they are all down here, who is flying the plane?"

His mother assured him that there was someone else still up there.

44. That Family Are Snobs

Coming home on leave after a couple of deep-sea voyages, I found my friends were always looking for parties, but were short of money. We went to one party in a friend's house. When we left and the door was shut behind us, someone said "What a snobbish family!"

I asked "Why snobbish? They did not seem snobbish to me!"

"Didn't you see the gin bottle on the sideboard?"

Me: "Yes!"

"What brand was it?"

Me: "Gordons"

"That's what I mean, that family are snobs, they wanted us all to believe they paid full price for it, that's why it was on show on the sideboard!"

At that time in Harwich and Dovercourt, nearly everyone drank smuggled Dutch Bols gin (and smoked Dutch tobacco). Bols could be obtained at £1 a bottle, about a third of the full duty-paid price. What really annoyed my friends was that the family did not drink the Gordons gin. They actually served Bols from a bottle kept at the back of the cupboard.

45. Why me?

We had been for a visit to the north and were returning to Heswall on the Wirral, in a hurry to get back for an extra Sunday afternoon choral rehearsal. Driving through the outskirts of Liverpool, I was singled out by the police and stopped.

"Do you know what the speed limit is here, Sir?"

"Er..40 I think" (suspecting it was thirty)

"It is 30 Sir, and you were clocked doing 45".

"Look officer, I was in a line of cars, and they were all doing 45 so why me?"

"Because you were the only one who pulled out to overtake!"

It was a fair cop, but he said that he had had a tiring day and he just wanted me to arrive home safely so he would let me off this time. We had a slow frustrating drive home not daring to exceed the speed limit, and made the rehearsal in the nick of time.

The Royal Navy

46. The Duck Billed Platypus

I applied for the 16 year old entry to the Royal Navy College at Dartmouth. I took the examination twice and did well in the written examinations. The first time I went for interview I was floored by two things. One, in the "crossing the swamp" teamwork exercise, I was not very quick climbing the monkey ropes. In an unguarded moment when asked how I had travelled to the interview I said " I came in one of the new Diesel Railcars". The head of the interview board said " We will ask you to give a five minute talk on a topic that arises naturally during our conservation - your topic will be " Diesel Railcars". I could hardly speak for five seconds on them, let alone five minutes.

So, at my second interview, I had practised and practised on the monkey ropes and I was determined not to say anything about any subject upon which I could not speak for five minutes. They asked me which countries I would like to visit. "Australia," I said. "Tell us a bit about Australia!", so I went through the list of Sydney Harbour bridge, the Aboriginals, kangaroos, wallabies, the duck billed platypus....the head of the Interview Board said "Stop there. We will ask you to give a five minute talk on a subject that arises naturally in our conversation, your topic will be The Duck Billed Platypus". I had fallen into the trap again.

When I joined the Merchant Navy, my first trip was to Australia and I thought that I would visit the animal that had caused me so much trouble. I took a ferry to Taronga Park Zoo in Sydney. I waited for about three hours by its enclosure, and it did not appear. In recent years Ann and I have been back three times and still haven't seen one. I am beginning to think the same as the early settlers. They thought it was a hoax!

47. If you want advice ask the Royal Navy

The founding of the Nautical Institute brought the Royal and Merchant Navies in closer contact than they had been before, to share expertise and experience, but there was always a bit of rivalry.

After a hard day's work at a seminar on navigation and collision avoidance, we were relaxing after dinner and "swinging the lamp" talking about a few near misses and lucky escapes.

One of the RN officers had had a few more glasses of wine than the rest of us and announced loudly:

"If you want to know anything about proper Ship Handling and Navigation you should ask the RN!"

Me: "Hang on a minute, the RN's record is not perfect, is it?"

"Ah! I can explain!"

He then described five accidents to RN ships, the first four of which I knew nothing about. In none of them was the RN to blame, apparently. I am still working out why the chain ferry at Devonport was to blame when hit by a naval ship, or London bridge for that matter, or forgetting that when you are heading up the Channel and pass the Greenwich Meridian, the minutes of longitude increase towards the right hand side of the chart, not the left.

The MN is not perfect either and we have a lot to learn from each other.

48. Multiple Choice

Multiple choice tests are difficult to set but easy to mark. A colleague warned us about an alleged malpractice (or brilliant idea, depending on your point of view) which had reputedly occurred in the police sergeants' examinations. Those examinations were at one time marked using a plastic sheet with holes cut to reveal the correct answers. Some bright spark passed the word around that if you ticked every box; you got full marks every time. Armed with this warning Liverpool Polytechnic devised a new marking policy +1 for a tick in the right box, -1 for a tick in the wrong box. We incorporated it in the test for a tape/slide programme on the 1972 changes in the Regulations for Preventing Collisions at Sea (Colregs).

I was invited to HMS "Dryad", the Royal Navy's navigation school, to demonstrate the programme, and I asked the RN lecturers if they would mind trying out the new test. After the test, one of the lecturers said in a rather "plummy" voice "I say old chap – I don't like your new marking system. I've finished up with a minus quantity!"

Despite his protestation that they were still teaching the old rules until the entry-into-force date of the amendments, I was not convinced. I was quite pleased because I earlier told a joke which included remarks in a scouse accent and he had shouted out "Now we know where he really comes from!" I am pleased to be an honorary scouser, but I was born in London.

49. References

I had been a keen and reasonably successful Sea Scout, becoming a Patrol Leader, gaining my First Class badge and getting a "Charge Certificate" to take charge of the scout boat "Venturer" etc.

In 1952 when I applied for entry into Dartmouth Royal Naval College, the Group Scout Master, Mr Clark, who had been a lowly Commissioned Gunner in the Royal Navy in World War ll, gave me a glowing reference. When I asked our senior Scoutmaster, Hugh Wake, he politely refused to give me a reference at all. He had family connections with a long historical line of Admirals and the reference would have carried some weight. Mr Clark asked him on my behalf and he again refused. I was disappointed because he was a very nice man, he did a lot for me at 4th Dovercourt Sea Scouts and I got on well with him.

More than 40years later, I was talking to his son Philip, whom I had recently interviewed for the Nautical Institute and who is the top man in that organisation. I told him the story about the references and he said; "My father would not give me a reference for the RN either, so like you I joined the Merchant Navy." We worked out that his father had not enjoyed Navy life and thought that we would not enjoy it either. He was being kind. Certainly in my case I think he was right and I thoroughly enjoyed my career in the MN.

50. War Trophy

The Royal Fleet Auxiliary is the Merchant Navy "arm" of the Royal Navy and supplies and supports the fleet. I was very privileged to be invited to sail in the RFA tanker "Grey Rover" during the rehearsal for a NATO "Sea Day". This is when all the NATO hierarchy are shown what the combined NATO fleets can do.

We sailed from Portland and the day's action was non-stop with refuelling at sea, depth charges, gun firing, air exercises, helicopter activities etc.

When things calmed down a bit I was invited into the Officer's Wardroom and was surprised to see a cabinet

RFA Grey Rover

containing a "war trophy". It was part of a submarine conning tower with a maple leaf on it. I said "has this ship been in action?" and "I thought that Canada was on our side?"

Apparently Grey Rover was one of the first fleet tankers to have "a variable pitch propeller" which could be "feathered", still rotating, but the ship not going anywhere. The Canadian submarine had heard the propeller turning and decided it was safe, because by the time they surfaced, the tanker would have gone. Unfortunately it hadn't and the propeller took a chunk out of the conning tower.

That is what exercises are for. If they go exactly according to plan, you learn nothing.

51. Commander Fox

Ann and I were invited to a cocktail party on the Nuclear Submarine Support Vessel H.M.S. "Wakeful" in Liverpool

Docks. It was a good party and we stayed on talking to the Commanding Officer, who said that he was interested in joining the Nautical Institute. I was the local Branch Secretary and I promised to drop an application form in on my way to the Radar School the following morning. The ship had recently been pilloried in the press as HMS "Wasteful" as it had been bought at great expense from Sweden, and then had a long and costly fitting out. I owed the CO a favour too because he had been most upset when Ann told him that to her, his ship looked just like a tug. He admitted that it was really a tug, but nuclear submarines have to have something to tow them home if they have problems.

Approaching the ship in the cold, misty, light of morning, with a bit of a headache, I realised that I could remember the CO's name, but not his rank. There was a rating on sentry duty at the gangway. He was not smiling. Knowing how touchy RN officers are if you verbally demote them, I decided to give the CO the rank of Commander.

"I have some documents here for Commander Fox".

"There is no Commander Fox on this ship sir".

Start again.

"I have some documents here for Lieutenant Commander Fox".

"There is no Lieutenant Commander Fox on this ship sir".

"Yes there is, I was on board yesterday evening. I met him, and had a long conversation with him".

"There is NO Lieutenant Commander Fox on this ship sir!"

"Who is your Commanding Officer then?"

"Commander Wolf sir!".

It had been a good party.

Liverpool Polytechnic Radar School

52. Rain on the Radar

My first teaching job was at the Radar School at Gladstone Dock. In order to get good radar signals, it was placed very close to the dock wall, over what had been the proposed second lock entrance to the dock. When it was built, there was only very loose infill underneath and the builders had to dig very deep to find a firm foundation. Having spent so much on the foundations, there was very little money left for a roof. The roof was very fragile – it leaked. If water came dripping through onto the radars, we would ask Liverpool Corporation to repair it. They would send men in hob-nail boots who would walk on the roof, repair the original leaks, but make several more.

Part of the Radar Observer examination was a practical, in which the candidate had to get an optimum "picture" and find things in sea clutter from waves, and rain clutter echoes from rain. If it was blowing hard from the North West and raining, they had a proper test. If it was calm, fine weather, the examiner's first question was "What does rain look like on the radar?"

One young India Steamship cadet knew the answer. "It comes through a hole in the roof, drips down onto the radar screen here, and trickles down onto the floor here!" A novel answer, but he was telling it as it is!

53. The Special Short-Range Radar

The first time I was given responsibility as a Course Leader, it was for a special radar course for Manchester Ship Canal Pilots. Radar in confined waters has special problems, largely because radar that is designed to detect things 48 miles away, is far too powerful for things a few feet away.

Associated Electrical Industries (AEI) designed a special radar for Manchester Ship Canal Company and I was invited to see it one Saturday morning on board the tug "Manchester Talisman". The mate of the tug offered to switch it on for us, and I watched as he went through the starting sequence that we taught at the Radar School. Having set the controls to minimum and switched on, he walked very deliberately round to the back of the radar and gave it a hearty kick, then came back and finished the setting up in the usual way.

I whispered to the AEI representative, "What was all that about?"

"Ah!" he said "A bit embarrassing really. The last radar they had, had a sticky relay switch and you needed to kick the radar. The Mate thinks kicking the radar is part of the normal setting up procedure. There is no need to do it on this one, but we hadn't the heart to tell him!"

Shortly after this, the radar transmitter caught fire, (nothing to do with the above incident). So we just stayed chatting for a bit before going home. Some pilots had told me "Even when you cannot see the canal banks in thick fog we know which way to steer just by looking at the towline – after all we know the tug is in the canal ahead of us". I was somewhat alarmed when the tug skipper said "In thick fog we know which way to steer just by looking at the tow line and lining up with it – after all we know the ship is in the canal astern of us!" There is a worrying inconsistency here. Both ship and tug are watching the towline and no one is looking at where they are going.

54. The Guinness Boats

Part of my research into short-range radars was carried out by kind permission of the Managers and Masters of the ships running from Dublin with bulk Guinness, going up the Ship Canal to the bottling plant in Manchester.

One evening we were approaching Stanlow Oil refinery when the radar screen was covered in false echoes. Usually, false echoes are the result of multiple radar reflections and each time the energy is reflected, it gets weaker, so the false echoes are weak. In this case they were far stronger than the real echoes.

I called the Second Mate over and said "Do you know what these are?" "Yes! They are false echoes". "I know they are false echoes, but do you know what causes them?" He said "I used to worry a lot about those, even lying awake at night worrying about what caused them. But now, I don't worry about them at all!" I asked "So you found out what was causing them?" "No Sir, I did not! But I discovered that if you collided with them, you did not do any damage at all!"

A nice laid-back philosophy, but not one I could use in my teaching. Eventually we found that they came from the oil tanks in the refinery, caused by strong transmissions leaking out of the back of the parabolic scanner.

The second Mate explained that, when you approached the swing bridges, multiple radar echoes made it look as if there were about five or six bridges. "Fortunately", he said, "When one opens, they all open!" Another problem solved.

He told me that the ships – which had no gyro compass – tried out an automatic pilot based upon the magnetic compass. It worked well on the sea passage. It was so good they tried it in the canal. It steered very well in straight sections. It came unstuck when the magnet in the compass detected the first swing bridge, and as it opened, tried to follow it.

55. The Old Men on the Dock

The Radar School was really the end of the world, about a mile from the dock gates. There were two old men who worked just outside the school, repairing the very heavy wooden fenders, decking and piling of the dock. We felt very sorry for them. The radar course finished at 4 p.m. each day and we got into our car and drove off, just as they started their long trek round to the dock gate, in rain, snow or summer heat. We offered to give them a lift. They were horrified. "Good Lord! No thank you! That would be no good at all! You see, we knock off at 5 p.m. and it takes us an hour to reach the gate. If you gave us a lift, we would have to work another 50 minutes!!"

One summer day they were just sitting on a bollard all day, not working. We said "Is there a problem?" "No problem at all. We have done all the repairs that were needed and are waiting for something else to break!"

Not long after that a Harrison Line ship was caught by a gust of wind, the stern tug's line broke and it nearly sailed into the Radar School. Our two old gentlemen were set up with work until they retired.

56. Measuring Distances

I sailed with one Master in Blue Funnel, who had made a practice of estimating distances by eye. He would say confidently "That lightship is 1.5 miles off", or "We are 9 miles off that island". I tried to catch him out by checking on the radar. He noticed and said, "It is no use you checking – I know I am right!" I never did catch him out.

At the Radar School, I would take students out onto the dock wall, ask them to estimate the distance of a ship or buoy, and then check on the radar. The reason for doing this was that in thick fog, they could relate what they saw on the radar to what they would have seen by eye on a good day.

I tried the same with pilots and got a surprise. "How far off is that buoy?" I asked. "A number 4 iron, a pitch and two putts!" was the reply. Some pilots spend a lot of time waiting for ships.

57. Interesting Visits

Several of the organisations on Merseyside, including the Nautical Institute, Chartered Institute of Transport and Honourable Company of Master Mariners used to take branch members on visits.

One of the most interesting was Shell Oil's Research Centre at Thornton, Cheshire. It was very interesting to see and hear about research. One really unusual request they had received originated with a trombone player complaining that his slide was sticking. The question asked of Shell was "What is the best oil to use on a trombone slide?" After carrying out the research, the right product was found and the client said "I would like to buy some". "We normally sell it in 40 gallon drums!". "Well, if that is the only way to buy it, I will take 40 gallons". As he went away, the Shell people felt bad about the fact that he had had to buy far too much for his needs – even if his trombone was very sticky, 40 gallons would last him several lifetimes.

Imagine their surprise, when he came back about six months later, said how well the oil worked and asked for another 40 gallons! Shell found out later that he was putting it into small bottles, labelling it "Trombone Oil". He had found and filled a gap in the music shop market!

58. Changing Behaviour

1982 A New Simulator

On the Radar Simulator Course, the students learn as much from one another as they do from the lecturers. These are proud professional mariners who usually have more than 10 years experience. Letting the Master of a coaster navigate the QE2 or vice versa, lets them see "How others see us".

You brief them, put them into a complex traffic situation, give them control, see what happens, then do a de-brief to see what lessons have been learned.

When the Masters and Mates of coasters and dredgers started to come on the courses, it was a real eye-opener. A lot of experience, little formal training, often learning from shipmates (the "sitting by Nellie" principle) and picking up other peoples' bad habits.

At the end of a course, as they were leaving, I said to a coaster Master "Was the course useful?"   He said "Wow! The main thing I have learned is that for the last twenty years I have been doing very dangerous things, without even realising it!"

I was pleased and suggested "So now you will do things differently?"

He thought for a moment, then replied "I wouldn't go that far! I expect I will do the same as I have always done, but I will worry much more!"

59. Randalls Sluices

With radar, as with other things, a little knowledge can be a dangerous thing. I read in one of the Navigation Journals about a strange phenomenon in the Straits of Messina between Italy and Sicily.   When they put a power cable across the Strait, the radar only "saw" the little part of the cable that was at 90 degrees to the radar beam. So it looked like a little fishing boat directly under the cable. If you altered course to port or starboard the reflection moved with you. In clear weather that did not matter, you could see there was no boat there, but in fog, you worried. I had been through the Strait and seen it.

Coming down the Ship Canal on a clear afternoon, with the pilot on the bridge wing to make sure things were safe, I was trying to navigate from the radar, as if we were in fog. All went well until we got to Randalls Sluices, where a power cable crosses the canal. Having experienced the effect in the Straits of Messina, I knew that the echo in the middle of the canal was likely to be the part of the cable that was at 90 degrees to the radar beam. I reported this to the pilot. He invited me to come outside and take a look. It might well have been the power cable that was showing, but it was also a dredger, working in the middle of the canal, right under the cable. It was a good job it was a clear day.

60. Using the Big Radar in Lake Erie

After teaching for three years at the Radar School, I did a voyage to the Great Lakes, to get data for my research degree and teaching material for my lectures.

79

It had been a sunny spring morning in Toronto and dozens of yachtsmen had taken advantage of the good weather to go for a sail on Lake Erie. In the afternoon, it was foggy and they were all returning to harbour just as the "Manchester Port" was leaving for Detroit.

"Manchester Port" had two radars – a large 16" Decca with all the modern "bells and whistles" on it, and a smaller 9 inch or 12 inch basic set. I was asked to man the radar. It was a real test. The big screen was covered with echoes. I then noticed a small echo right astern of us and thought we must have hit something. Rushing to the bridge wing I looked aft and saw a paint can in the wake, which had been tossed overboard by a seaman. (A very serious misdemeanour in these environmentally friendly days).

The Master came over to me, looked at the big radar and said "Don't use that one. You see too much on it, use the small one, its easier!" I was astonished that he should advise me to miss some of the echoes by using the smaller radar. As in many things, the older man was right. On the big radar, in the flat calm of the lake, you saw every seagull and piece of flotsam on the water, and the real yachts could be missed amongst all the unwanted echoes. On the small radar you saw only what you needed to see.

61. Bad Back

I was in the garage on a cold winter night, busy building the Mirror Dinghy "Bee" from a kit that Ann had given me. At a certain point, I needed to lift the boat and turn it over. The family were all warm and snug watching TV indoors, so I tried to do it without help. To cut a long story short, I strained my back, and have had bouts of back pain ever since. It causes the family some amusement when it catches me and I walk round bent over and rigid. I spent what seemed like hours head first in the cucumbers in our cold frame one afternoon. On another occasion I seized up at the Mersey Tunnel entrance and we had to get the Tunnel Police to take son Nick to catch the Liverpool football supporters' train to Ipswich, and friends Keith and Sheila Jones to rescue me and the car.

The most worrying moment was when I was teaching Manchester pilots on a radar course and they noticed I was in some pain. One of them offered to take me into a corner at lunch time and "Lay his hands on me". His colleagues said he was OK but a bit eccentric, notably that he thought he had a Red Indian sitting on his shoulder, taking care of him. Whatever the truth, I did not relish the help offered.

Between coffee and lunch time, I had to pretend I was better. It was going well until I dropped the chalk. It was agony bending nonchalantly to pick it up, but I managed it somehow!

62. High Speed Jet Foils

British and Irish Ferries were going to introduce Boeing Jetfoil High Speed Ferries between Dublin and Liverpool and asked Liverpool Polytechnic to put on a special course on high-speed navigation and collision avoidance. We agreed, we did our homework and were ready. Three weeks before the service was due to start, not one of the officers had been on the course, so I rang the Marine Superintendent in Dublin.

Me: "You asked for this course. Do you want it or not?"

Him "You are embarrassing me now. Yes, we do want the course. You see, it is all right for you clever b…..s in Liverpool, you know all the answers. In Dublin, we are still trying to find out the questions!"

You may laugh at the remark, but he was right. They had just taken delivery of the ferries and Boeing were busy teaching them how to control the engines, steering and other technicalities. Until they "knew the answers" to handling the craft, coming to Liverpool and dashing round at 35 knots on the simulator would have been a waste of time. For example you could not choose to do 10, 15, or 20 knots to get out of trouble, because you were either up on the foils doing about 30 knots or sitting in the water doing about 5-7 knots.

They did the course and were competent before the service started.

63. Fixing the Position off a Featureless Coast

When navigating along a long low coastline like the Netherlands, using radar for position fixing, you have two problems. One is that the coast does not show up very well, and you could well be taking ranges from an inland railway embankment that follows the contours of the coast. Use that to plot your position and you are in trouble. The other problem is that if there are no islands or headlands, you know how far OFF the coast you are, but not how far ALONG it. Modern technology has solved the problem.

I was testing an overseas student in its use and described the situation as above.

Me "How would you fix your position along the coast?"

Him "Bacon, Sir!"

Me "Bacon??"

Him "Yes Sir! Bacon! Bacon on the Rudder!"

I wondered if he had discovered something that I did not know, but eventually I realised he meant "Beacon on the Radar", which was the correct answer.

In these day of multi-cultural crews such misunderstandings in a crisis could lose valuable time in getting things done, so training is more important than ever.

64. Being Caught Cheating

In the Radar Observer Examination the desks were set widely apart and the room was quiet, when I caught a glimpse of a piece of blotting paper floating to the floor. Moments later it was picked up by someone in the next row. I pretended to look the other way. It then floated to the floor again and was picked up by the original candidate. I walked quietly over to the pair of them, picked up the "evidence" which had been written upon in blue in one handwriting and black in another. Not wanting to disturb the examination, I led them gently by the collar to my office outside.

"You have both failed for cheating!"

It was not until this point that I read what they had written:

"What is an Interscan Cursor?" in blue and below it in black "I don't know."

I changed the ruling to "You have both failed for trying to cheat!" Proper cheating would have barred them from the examination for six months, but we took pity on them and allowed them to resit later that month. The British are not very good at cheating.

Liverpool Polytechnic

65. Jokes and Notes

The Masters Class was full and they were taking down notes on Navigational Aids. As usual, I was putting a few "funnies" into the lecture to see who was awake. The room was quiet when a pen was slammed onto the desk at the back:

"I'm about b….. fed up with this lot!!"

"What's the matter Mr Murphy?"

"Do you mind telling me which are the notes and which are the jokes, 'cos I'm putting it all down here!"

66. Having Trouble

A little old man came into my office when I was Head of Maritime Studies, leaned over my desk and said:

In a whisper "I am having trouble with my dicker, Sir"

Me: "Pardon?"

Even quieter "I am having trouble with my dicker, Sir"

Me: "Well, I am sorry, but I don't think I can help"

"Dicker, Sir, Dicker Navigator!"

Me: "Oh, Decca Navigator. So what is the problem?"

"Well, I passed my certificates and then decided I did not want to go to sea any more and for 15 years I worked ashore. When I decided to go back to sea, they had fitted this new Decca Navigator thing. All the other officers could use it, but I did not know how to switch it on, how to take the readings or plot the position. When you are in the middle of the North Sea, lost, and eight miles from where you thought you were, the old heart starts thumping a bit, Sir."

Me: "Well that's easy, we can explain it all for you"

Half a day later he went away able to switch the Decca on, set it up, take readings, apply corrections and get a fix. He went away happy.

Not the only thing

A few days later the same old man came back into my office, leaned over my desk and said:

Whisper "Thanks for teaching me about Decca, but that was not the only thing. I am having trouble with my radar as well. You know in heavy seas you get a lot of "clutter" near the centre of the screen. Well, I remember from my radar course that there is one of the controls that gets rid of it, but I cannot remember which one!"

Me: "It is the Anti Sea Clutter Control"

"I thought it might be. But that is not my only problem. The Master of my ship is a liar. He said I was off the bridge for 15 minutes making myself a cup of tea, and the other ship went past 50 feet off. That was a complete lie! I was only off the bridge for 5 minutes and the other ship was at least 150 feet off, I saw it go past! There were quite heavy seas and I had picked up the other ship on the radar at about 12 miles. I watched it getting closer. Then I admit my mistake. When it went into the sea clutter, I forgot all about it."

So he had a little radar refresher course, but it made me worry about the officer shortage and the advertising campaign at that time, trying to get "ancient mariners" to go back to sea again.

67. Death off Iceland

In today's changing world you cannot be sure of continued employment and one of my former students had been on the phone for days to agents and shipping companies without success. Eventually he decided he had done enough for the week and tried to ring a friend to invite him for a round of golf. He did not get through to his friend. The phones were playing up, and he got a "crossed line" and found himself listening to two other people talking. They were bemoaning the fact that they could not find an officer for their ship, and were getting desperate. To cut a long story short, he butted into the conversation, offered his services and got the job. He very happily told me about his good fortune. Some months later, I read to my great dismay that his ship had run aground off the coast of Iceland, seemingly abandoned after some catastrophe, very much like the "Mary Celeste". I mourned the loss of a very likeable and enthusiastic officer whose luck seemed to have run out. Imagine my amazement when I bumped into him a few weeks later. I told him "I thought you were dead! Wasn't that your ship that was found abandoned off Iceland?" "Yes, it was my ship, but I had done a few voyages and thought I would take a voyage off!" So his luck had not run out after all.

68. Better teaching this time

Three weeks into the term and the Masters' class was settling down well. I thought I recognised one of the Nigerian students in the front row, so I thought I would ask:

"Mr Niagwan, Have you been in my class before?"

"Yes Sir! About three years ago, but don't worry, the lecturing is better this time!"

69. Christmas Voyage

As Christmas time was approaching we were all looking forward to a break. I had a telephone call from one of the local shipping agents asking if any of our Masters class wanted to do a short voyage down to the Canary Islands over Christmas to make some money. The ship was in Runcorn on the Manchester Ship Canal.

Several students were interested, but between them they agreed that the one with the greatest need was a married man with children and a mortgage and they offered it to him.

There was very bad weather in the Bay of Biscay over Christmas and the small ship was lost with all hands. I was shocked and sad. I lost sleep thinking of the plight of the lost student and his devastated family.

Imagine my surprise on the first day of term to see him sitting in the classroom. I was very happy but my first remarks were not very kind: "You are supposed to be dead!" He explained that he had gone aboard the ship in Runcorn, found the ship was in a very poor state of repair and the Master was drunk, so he decided not to take the job. He said "I was desperate for money, but not THAT desperate!"

I thought twice about passing on job opportunities after that.

70. Our "Mary"

We were very pleased when "Mary" passed her watch keeping examinations and went back to sea as a certificated Third Mate. "Mary" was a demanding student. Each time she failed, it was someone else's fault, not hers. Either the lecturer did not explain things properly, or he set too much homework and she could not keep up. It was never her fault, and she was very vocal in her complaints. We were delighted when she passed.

A few weeks later her father, who was a well-respected senior shipmaster came to the college on a radar simulator course. He called me aside and asked me to thank all the staff for their hard work in helping "Mary". He said the family were delighted when she passed, and without hesitation I said "We were all delighted too!"

He then went on to say that "Mary" had had a strange crisis of confidence when she went back to sea. She imagined the Master leaving her alone on the bridge of a huge container ship in the Straits of Dover with ships going everywhere and her not being able to cope. He had reassured her by saying "Look, "Mary", if you get the ship into trouble, the Master will lose his Certificate of Competency as well as you losing yours. When you think you are on your own, he will be on the deck below, keeping an eye on things and ready to be there to support you if things are getting on top of you".

What a nice supportive Dad, I thought, giving her such wise advice. As he walked away, he spoiled it all by saying "Mind you, if the Master knew my "Mary" like I know my "Mary", he wouldn't trust her with a bicycle, let alone a container ship!"

71. A Glowing Reference

We started Master of Science Courses at the Polytechnic, aimed at senior managers who were responsible not only for technical and operational matters but needed to deal with legal, financial and commercial matters as well. It was not easy to achieve Masters Degree level studies in such diverse fields, but the following was written to us by a satisfied Nigerian graduate;

"Thank you so much for the excellent course in Maritime Law. I now understand the law better than the judge, and if I explain it to him politely, I win all my cases".

You cannot do much better than that!

72. The Integration Problem

Nigerian Ports Authority needed qualified Master Mariners as Harbour Masters and in other senior posts. They sent many young men to Liverpool and we enjoyed teaching them. They were cheerful and enthusiastic. Liverpool, with its long connections with West Africa through Elder Dempsters, Palm Line, Niger Line etc, had plenty of things for them to do to make them feel at home and a local Nigerian community in the Princes Park area of the city.

I was therefore taken aback when a senior manager from Lagos came to see me and said that the training in Liverpool was not working out, and they were going to take all the students away and send them elsewhere.

The reason he gave was that "Liverpool has an integration problem!"

I thought I was on a winner as I explained how well the students mixed with the local community and how much they enjoyed their time with us. There was never any hint of racial or cultural problems – the integration problem, in my view, did not exist."

He then stopped me in my tracks by saying "The integration problem in Liverpool is that they integrate so well, they will not come home!"

I had lost my argument!

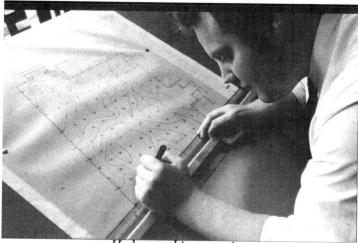

Hydrographic surveying

73. The Survey Launch

Teaching Hydrographic Surveying needs a special sort of teacher and George Singleton was one of the best. They would go off to some estuary or coastline as a bunch of individuals and come back as a team having carried out a challenging piece of work to high standards.

In order to give them experience in a proper survey launch, when Mersey Docks and Harbour Board got a new survey launch, we bought their old one (at a knock down price as we agreed to lend it back to them when required). The Polytechnic did not give us enough money to do proper dry docking and maintenance, so as the years went by, I used to lay awake thinking of the trauma and expense of it sinking at its mooring in the dock and having to be salvaged and removed. We decided to sell it "as is" without having its bottom surveyed.

We had two or three potential buyers. George took one potential buyer out on the Mersey and was cruising up and down at the normal low speed the students needed for surveying. The potential buyer said "Doesn't it go faster than this?" So George put the handle down and it shot off down the river at speed.

Unknown to us all was the fact that many hours of half speed running had filled the exhaust pipe with half-burnt fuel and debris and the sudden excitement caused it to catch fire, and ignite the cushions in the rear cabin for good measure.

When they looked astern, they were being followed by great clouds of black smoke and the occasional flame. George and the crew manfully put it out with foam extinguishers and came back to the Polytechnic to report to me.
I was in a meeting with some important visitors when George appeared, excited and looking as if he had fallen into a sack of soot and another of flour. I think my visitors wondered what sort of college we ran.

We eventually sold the launch at a profit (as it no longer had the lend-back clause in the contract). From then on we used a minibus towing a big dory as our survey vessel, which got to places more quickly and did not make people seasick.

74. The Sahara Desert

The Americans developed a military very long range, very low frequency navigation system called "OMEGA". Actually, they didn't, because the British Company Decca had invented it much earlier, but that is another story. They released the system for civil use, and part of my research was to try to discover if it was useful for merchant ships. Its military advantage was that nuclear submarines, which had to come near the surface to get higher frequency navigation signals, could receive Omega at depths that would not provide telltale "heat" trails on the surface. That would not help merchant ships.

Omega's accuracy was affected by the conductivity of the surface over which it travelled and one of my research students, Ibrahim Hussein from Egypt, came to register for a Master/Doctor of Philosophy Degree with us to look at the effect of the signals crossing, in particular, the Sahara Desert.

This is where the Council for National Academic Awards bureaucracy stepped in to thwart our efforts. They insisted that the research had to be carried out in the UK. I explained that there were plenty of reports on the operation of Omega in Europe, I wanted to carry out our observations at the Arab Maritime Transport Academy in Alexandria.

I tried to persuade them that moving the Sahara desert to Liverpool was not an option for us, and they insisted that granting a degree for work in Eygpt was not an option for them. So Ibrahim enjoyed his stay with us, studied widely and went home wiser, but without a higher degree. A great pity – he deserved one more that some people.

75. The Alternative

Whilst Head of Department at Liverpool Polytechnic, I was approached by a member of staff who was teaching Tanker Practice. He wanted an Explosimeter to demonstrate to students – an instrument to measure the concentration of flammable gases, in order to prevent explosions. I wrote to a well-known Instrument Maker and received the following reply: "We do not stock the Explosimeter which you have requested, but we think the attached product may meet your requirements" It was calibrated in decibels and would measure the loudness of the explosion! Not quite what we had in mind!

76. Negotiation: Arsenal v Liverpool

In the late 1970s as Head of Department of Liverpool Polytechnic, I ordered books from a supplier in North London. The acknowledgement of the order said "No goods can be supplied unless the money has been received!". Liverpool Council's Rules stated that "No money is to be paid until the goods are received". Deadlock. We negotiated. Still deadlock.

Liverpool Football Club were playing Arsenal the following Saturday.

Eventually the supplier agreed to send the books on three conditions:

1. The bill was paid immediately the books were received.

2. Liverpool did not pick Ian Rush.

3. Liverpool would give Arsenal a one goal start.

The books were delivered and the bill paid, but I was unable to meet the other conditions. Shame!

77. Persuasion and Dire Consequences

Bringing students from Libya to be educated in the UK, gave us a few unusual problems. Being strict followers of Islam, they were not familiar with Western customs or culture. Two students joined a 4 year degree programme which involved one year in college, a year at sea, and two years back in college. These two finished their first year's studies and passed their examinations and in July went off to sea, to learn about the practical side of nautical studies. In November they arrived back in my office and said: "We want to resume our studies".

I said "Your second year does not start until September next year. You are supposed to spend one whole year at sea".

"Do you know, that is exactly what the Master of our ship said when we arrived into Avonmouth and asked to leave!"

Me "He was quite right!" They indicated that the Master had changed his mind when they threatened him with a knife.

Another Libyan student who was unfamiliar with western life discovered girls and spent a wild first year at parties and dancing and only averaged 11% in his first year examinations. The pass mark was 40%. He appealed to me as Chairman of the Examination Board, to let him pass and go into the second year. He said "If I fail and I am sent back to Libya, I shall be shot!" I told him that, as Chairman, I could not decide whether he passed or failed, that depended on his answers in the examination and the marks given by the examiners. I did agree to look at the marked papers over the weekend, to see whether I thought he deserved a few more marks. On Monday morning I told him that the examiners had been too generous, and I thought he only deserved 9%. He said "But I will be shot!" I told him that with marks as low as that he deserved to be shot. He left the Polytechnic and disappeared.

A few months I was walking past the First Class carriages of the London train at Lime Street station, and saw him sitting in splendour, in a Saville Row suit, with gold cufflinks and tiepin and an expensive leather briefcase.

I looked the other way. Whatever he was doing, it was probably not legal, and I did not want to know!!

78. Can you trust Librarians?

Librarians are nice people. We have several in our family. Their skills and helpfulness are often not appreciated as much as they should be. At Liverpool Polytechnic, the Librarian kept offering to take charge of, and lend to students, the very expensive videos that we had bought with the Maritime Studies Department budget to be used in our lecture programmes. For a long time, I had kept them in a drawer, securely locked and lent them only to staff members. In a weak moment I agreed to let the Librarian take charge and he took them away to the library.

About three or four months later, he came back to me and said "Do you remember the video on Emergency Lifeboat Radio Procedures? Well, I want a new copy".
My reply was "Well, there you are! I told you that you would lose the videos if we let you take control of them! I suppose it has been borrowed and not returned?"

The Librarian said that was not the case at all. The system was working extremely well. Every student going to take his or her oral examinations used the video to brush up on radio procedure before going off to the Examination. They still had the video, but it was worn out through constant use.

Any training material that is so well used that it gets worn out, is doing a brilliant job, so I congratulated them and bought them a new one.

Since leaving Liverpool Polytechnic and working with video-suppliers Videotel Marine International, I have made it a company rule that any customer who returns a video worn out, can have a replacement free of charge.

79. A Cautionary Tale

Not long after I became Head of Maritime Studies, at about 1.30 p.m. one afternoon, I was sitting a my desk when a man in his 50's, dressed smartly in a yachting blazer and flannels knocked on my door and introduced himself. He told me his story. He said he was a former student of the Department, and was back in the UK after working with NASA on space projects in the USA. He had a yacht and was cruising round the UK coast. The Department had been so helpful to him in his early days that he wanted to say "Thank you!" and meet a few of the people he knew.

I congratulated him on his success in life, showed him round to meet people and we talked about some of the staff he remembered in the old days, Captain Twentyman, Commander Coffee, Captain Ferryman, Captain Ossie Stewart etc When he took his leave of me, I gave him my business card and we said our farewells.

At about 5.15 pm, still in my office, I had a phone call from the Head of the Transport and General Workers Union office just up the hill. The conversation went something like this:

Him "Am I speaking to Len Holder, Head of Maritime Studies at Liverpool Polytechnic?"

Me: "Yes"

Him (angrily) "Where is my whisky?"

Me "I don't know what you are talking about!"

Him: "You are Len Holder, Head of Maritime Studies at Liverpool Polytechnic, right? About a couple of hours ago you came to my office, gave me your business card and told me you had some spare whisky on your yacht, and I could have a case of it for £25! I gave you the £25 and you said you would be back by 5 pm. I want my whisky!!"

I tried to explain that we had both been "had" by a confidence trickster, but I don't think he believed me.

The moral to this story, is "Be careful to whom you give your business card!"

80. Letter from Wolverhampton

When course fees for overseas students were increased to several thousand pounds, some had difficulty paying. In order to help them, we admitted them to the course and allowed them to pay late, but this did not work as some had still not paid as the examinations drew near, so the Polytechnic made a rule: Fees for one year MSc programmes had to be paid by Christmas or they could not return to the classroom in January.

One Nigerian student said his family had enough money, but the difficulty was getting foreign exchange out of the country. He said he would go home at Christmas to sort it out. He did not arrive for the start of the spring term.

In the middle of January, I received a letter from the tutor of Wolverhampton Jail saying "One of my inmates wants to know if you can complete an MSc by correspondence".

Very sadly, he had tried legitimate means to get his money out, but he was from the wrong tribe and people were being awkward. Then someone said they would give him the money if he delivered a small parcel for them in Wolverhampton. He did not ask what was in the parcel. When he arrived in the UK and was asked at the airport "Did anyone give you anything to carry?" he showed them the parcel. It contained drugs and he was jailed for five years. The other inmates were sorry for him, they said he was innocent and should not be there. My secretary helped to look after his family. He did not finish the MSc but became a devout Christian while in prison, working in religious circles when he was freed.

Another Nigerian student with similar problems obtained cash in Lagos to pay his fees. They were newly printed forgeries and not very good ones at that. When he arrived in the UK he tried to pay the taxi driver with one. The taxi driver locked the cab doors and drove straight to the police station near Heathrow airport. The student was deported.

Very unfair for young and innocent people.

81. Contraband Whisky

I had thought hospices must be sad places, but visiting George Singleton at Southport, I learned otherwise. A colleague, Bill Dineley had thoughtfully wrapped up a bottle of George's favourite whisky and handed it to him when we arrived. George was having a wee dram and explaining that drinks are permitted in the hospice, when a nurse with a rattling "booze trolley" entered the ward. To our surprise, George grabbed his glass and the "contraband" bottle and hid them under the bedcovers.

Bill and I said "Why are you hiding it? We thought you said booze was allowed in here?"

George winked and said "It is. But this way I will have a glass from the nurse and then finish my own when she has gone!"

82. The Landlady and the Snake

The first group of Blue Star graduate entrants to the Merchant Navy had just passed their first watchkeeping examinations and had enjoyed their study time at the Polytechnic so much that they invited the staff to dinner at the Philharmonic pub on Hope Street. A young staff member asked my advice on what to wear. "You know students, jeans and a tee shirt I expect." They all came in smart suits and he wore jeans and a tee shirt and was not very happy with me.

I sat next to the only Polytechnic graduate in the group, who said "I don't expect you remember me?". I replied "Oh yes I do! You studied Physics at Plymouth Poly". In the course of his initial interview, three or four years earlier, he had told us that he stayed in a student bed-sit in which his landlord was a Royal Navy matelot, whose wife was Maltese. She had been a dancer in a Valetta bar, who performed her act with a snake. I repeated this story back to him word for word.

He mused "As I came up to Liverpool from Plymouth for that interview, I realised you must have a lot of applicants (in fact we had 2,341 for 24 places), so I needed to make myself memorable in some way, so whatever questions you asked me, I was determined to mention my landlady and her snake, and it worked!"

I was affronted that he thought our selection methods could be swayed by a mere anecdote. I carefully explained that, in order to interview a short list of about 200, we had to have very strict marking criteria. Each of the four members of the panel had a mark sheet on which the subjects from academic ability, through practical aptitude, leadership qualities, social attitudes etc were graded 1 to 10. The marks were collected and totalled to give a final score. I explained "It has to be absolutely rigorous, or by the time we reached number 200, we would have forgotten what number 1 was like!"

"Yes, I understand all that!" he said "But I am here, aren't I!!"

That set me wondering if he was right.

83. A Student with a Difference

I was admissions tutor to the BSc in Maritime/Nautical Studies for many years, but I only had one student who sat in front of me and opened the interview by saying "Right, I would like you to explain to me why I should come to Liverpool and not go to the degree course in Cardiff, Southampton or Plymouth!"   Fortunately, I passed the interview and Harry Hirst came to Liverpool to do his degree. He was a great student and very successful.

During his course, we had a Nautical Institute lecture on the latest developments in computers and navigational technology from a representative of the US equipment company Sperry Marine. The lecturer was proud of his company's exciting new equipment. "I thought we were going to see something really advanced" said a disappointed Harry. "What do you want?" asked the lecturer. "Well, the stuff you have shown all means I still have to go on board the ship to 'drive' it. What I want is automation and satellite links so that I can stay at home and drive the ship from my armchair!"

Many years later, Harry had become a successful lawyer, a partner in one of the top maritime law firms in Hong Kong. Having dinner with him during one of my visits, after the main course, he asked to be excused. He came back a few minutes later and we ordered dessert and coffee. "Sorry about that" he said "I had to make a phone call. You see, I had to have a ship arrested, and I thought if I waited until after dessert, I would be too late!" That is Harry, always full of surprises!

84. Yachtmasters

For seven years my colleague Alan Bole and I taught a winter evening class at Liverpool Polytechnic, leading to the Department of Transport Yachtmasters Examination. The same people came each winter and very few were really interested in passing the examination. It was a friendly group. They seemed to have great difficulty relating classroom theory to what went on at sea.

An example of this nearly ended in disaster. In college they had just learned all about siting the magnetic compass, keeping metal, magnetic material and electrical currents away from the binnacle. At the weekend two groups went to Llandudno to tow a boat

Alan Bole

back to Liverpool for winter lay-up. All went well until dusk, when it also started to get misty. The towing boat was heading east, but the boat being towed thought they were going west. They had turned on their temporary navigation lights. When they rigged the lights, they left a coil of wire below the compass and the electro-magnetic effect reversed the direction of the compass. This led to an argument with the other boat. They decided to head south until they could see the lights on the coast. But which south? They split the difference and actually finished up heading east, which was just as well.

They did not see the coast, but after a while waves started breaking heavily either side of the boat. They were in shallow water and about to go aground. They decided to send up distress rockets.

Instead of buying proper rockets, they had purloined some out-of-date ones from somewhere. Out of date rockets sometimes work properly, sometimes they do not work at all, and sometimes they ignite prematurely – which happened to them. The first rocket went off almost horizontally towards the shore. A courting couple in the sand dunes at Formby got a terrible shock. The rocket buried itself in the sand beside them. Incensed, the young man dug it out and took it to the Coastguard Station to complain. The Coastguard realised it was a distress rocket, asked "Where did it come from?" and called out the lifeboat. The men were rescued. They were later interviewed by the Liverpool Echo and a full report appeared including the fact that they were students of our Yachtmasters Class!

85. The Margherita

Mobil Shipping Company sponsored four cadets each year on the Liverpool Polytechnic Degree Course. The cost of a three-year degree on full pay, plus travel, books and all the courses needed for a watchkeeper, made this a very generous sponsorship. Competition was fierce, with over 100 applicants for the four places and Mobil spared no expense to make sure they selected the right people.

Each year, they chartered the Llandaff College training vessel "Margherita" and set off from a Bristol Channel port (Bristol or Barry), to carry out nautical exercises in the Bristol Channel and then go ashore to a hotel in Milford Haven for business games, individual interviews, group tasks etc. Setting this up, getting about 12 short-listed candidates, interviewers from Bull Holmes recruitment agency, Mobil and the Polytechnic together, was a logistical nightmare. So, even if the weather was awful, they were very reluctant to cancel and rearrange it.

On one occasion a nasty westerly was blowing up the Bristol Channel and the "Margherita" was leaping about a bit. The candidates, unused to the motion, quickly turned green and felt unhappy. To give them their due, some still crawled ashen-faced to the Interview Panel and gasped "What do you want me to do next, Sir?"

As the weather worsened, the interview panel themselves felt a bit off colour and decided to suspend the practical exercises. As it got worse still, even the redoubtable Captain Hugh Francis and the Llandaff crew began to feel a bit sea sick. Ships of about 120 to 150 feet in length are, to my mind, far more uncomfortable than a small boat or a large ship.

Amid all this mayhem, the engine room hatch flew open and a little Welshman appeared out of the diesel fumes to ask "Where's the beer then, I thought we were out here for a party?" He was a former Royal Navy Engineroom Artificer and obviously immune to the perils of small ships and diesel fumes. I admired his fortitude.

86. Interviewing University Graduates

The marking scheme for the Graduate Entrant interviews was based on a starting "score" of 5 and ranged from 0 to 10. If someone was good on leadership, having led expeditions in overseas countries etc, you would move the score up to 8 or 9, if they were loners and showed no sign of it, you would move them down to 3 or 2. The same with the other topics.

This worked well until Captain McPhail joined the panel. A bluff, competent and practical seaman, his approach was a bit unconventional. We had just had a candidate in front of us who was academically excellent, and had shown initiative by playing a role in student societies, taking a year out to edit a newspaper etc.

As chairman I asked Captain McPhail for his list of marks. Leadership 0, Academic Ability 0, Practical Aptitude 0 etc .... Total 0!. I said "Excuse me, Captain McPhail, no-one can be that bad. What made you give such low marks?" He replied "Looks like a bloody socialist to me!"

Bearing in mind the ethos and attitudes of Blue Star as a traditional, family owned company, I realise Bill Cannell would not fit. I made a note of his address and invited him to join the Polytechnic for a Research Degree, where he made a great contribution to the research team led by Keith Jones. Bill was later sent to the USA to present research findings and Sperry tried to "poach" him. Sperry was an arms manufacturer and Bill was not into that. He joined the environmental lobby and Dr Cannell was later to be seen on TV talking about the danger of trains carrying nuclear waste crashing and similar environmental topics.

87. The Entrepreneur

Blue Star Line rang me up one day and said: "We are going to sack one of the Graduate Entry Trainees, and are ringing as a courtesy to you, because you recruited him." I asked why they were sacking him. He was in jail in Saudi Arabia. He and a couple of the seamen had been trying to sell "dirty" postcards to some Arabs. He was the lookout and did not do his job well enough - they were caught. Blue Star could not have officers who had been in jail.

Bum Boats

I reminded them that every time I had been through the Suez Canal, Arab bum-boat men in Port Said had tried to sell me "dirty" postcards. I told them "Mrs Thatcher is Prime Minister and we live in 'Enterprise Britain'. She encourages entrepreneurs and would be pleased to think that one of her 'subjects' had turned the tables and was selling to the Arabs. She would be proud of him!"

They said "In that case we will not sack him!"

He became a junior officer. The story has a nice ending. His original degree was in mining engineering, and with a young family, when South Africa was booming he could not resist the high salaries and promotion that would result from a return to his original career interest. Later, when his family had grown up a bit and South Africa had become a troubled and less friendly country, he thought back to a time in his life to when he had been really happy, and returned to seafaring.

88. The Business Game

Part of the interview process for Mobil sponsorship was a business game in which the candidates had to "manage" a fleet of road tankers delivering petroleum throughout the UK. There were several depots, different products and many destinations and a work force who could work only limited hours and had "problems" – one had a hernia and could do only light work, another's wife was expecting a baby so he could not be sent on long runs etc. It was quite demanding.

On one occasion, a young Australian applicant who had paid his own way from "down under" to come for the interview, finished up way below all the other candidates in the game. Up until then, he had been one of the most promising of the bunch. We looked into it. Each time he had sent a tanker from, say, South Wales to Liverpool, he made it return to South Wales before sending it to pick up the next load in, for example, Newcastle. We asked why he did this. He said "I did not know if there was a road from Liverpool to Newcastle". We said "Well, you should have assumed that there was one".

His reply floored us. "In order to earn enough money to come here for interview, I got a job with AMPOL, the Aussie petroleum company, routing tankers all over Australia. If I had assumed there were roads between each of the destinations in Australia, I would soon have been in trouble, I can tell you!"

Thus it was that the only one who had actually done the job and gained experience, got the lowest marks. We did not let that count against him.

89. Personnel Management

For centuries maritime education has encouraged seafarers to be technically competent. Management of people has been a long way back in second place or might even be described as "failed to finish".

Talking to David Webb, one of the first Blue Star Line Graduate Entry officers at the end of his Masters Course: I said "How was the course?"

He replied "Rather disappointing. I now know all the jail sentences and fines for getting things wrong. I thought we were going to be taught how to do the job of a ship's Master!"

A very shrewd observation.

Management education for senior ship's staff could be taught much more effectively.

90. Student Welfare

The daughter of a mature student came to see me as the MSc examinations were about to start and said "I am very worried about my father. He is so 'wound up' about these examinations that I think, if he fails, he will harm himself. Could you please make sure he passes?" I said "Although

I chair the Exam Board, whether he passes or not depends on what he does in the examination and the marks awarded by all the examiners. Thank you for alerting me. I can assure you that we have a good welfare system, we will look after him, explain the appeals procedure and the possibility of re-sits, we will make sure he is OK." He failed but was well looked after and decided to sue the Polytechnic on the grounds that one lecturer in particular was incompetent – but that is another story.

Getting back to student welfare. A year later an African student came up to me and said "I am very worried about my friend. He is so wound up about the examination that if he fails, I think he will do something stupid!" I said "Don't worry, we have come across this problem before, we will look after him. I can assure you that we have a good welfare system, we will make sure he does not harm himself ......" Before I had finished he said "No Sir, No! You have got it all wrong! I don't think he will harm himself, I think he will do something to you!"

91. Examining at Sunderland Polytechnic

The problem with being an external examiner at another centre is that the examinations tend to all come at the same time of year, so it gets very busy. The only way I could fit it all in, was to fly from Manchester to Newcastle on the Dan Air Flight. I stood waiting for the plane to arrive from Cardiff with the only other passenger, a dear old lady in her 80s. "I had never flown before coming down here this week" she said "I was alright when I boarded the plane and got strapped in, and I was alright as we took off, but when

112

we got into level flight, the pilot turned round and said 'Does anyone want coffee?' and someone said yes, so he got up and served it himself. That had me really worried" She added "If the pilot asks this time, do you mind saying 'No!'"

Sure enough, when we took off and got into level flight, the pilot asked if anyone wanted coffee. She frantically signalled to me to say no, but someone else said yes and he came back to serve it. I was not really worried because I THINK there was a co-pilot in the other seat flying the plane. However, knowing Dan Air's reputation, maybe the old lady was right..

92. Civil Service Hospitality

Whilst carrying out research into the navigational accuracy of merchant ships, I worked closely with the Hydrographic Department in Taunton. I became friendly with Godfrey Murt, Head of the Automatic Cartography Section, who was introducing computer handling of chart data. Indeed Godfrey said that I was the first person from outside the Admiralty to ask him for charts in a computer-readable form, and the fact that I asked as an outsider, triggered a £14 million programme to computerise the charts.

Godfrey was working very closely with the US Hydrographic Office and had recently had a group over from Washington, working every day and late into every evening on their project. Godfrey took them to lunch in Taunton, and then after work, to dinner, and he claimed expenses on the usual Civil Service form. It came back with a note on the bottom saying "Officials at your level are allowed only ONE entertainment per day!" Godfrey wrote underneath "As we had lunch, spent the afternoon in a brothel, and then had dinner, I consider this was only one entertainment!" I understand that they paid it.

93. Putting your name down…..

I was at a very select party at the Guildhall in London. The group of gentlemen I was with were discussing who would be the next Lord Mayor.

A very pompous member of the group said "I would like to have been Lord Mayor, but do you know, you have to have your name down almost as soon as you are born. I was 26 when I decided and that was much too old!"

I decided to tell them, about an almost identical conversation I overheard on the top deck of an F19 bus from Birkenhead to Heswall.

Passenger (thick scouse accent) to conductor who was a friend: "Ehhrrr…what's your lad doing now then?"

Conductor (also scouse) "I wanted him to be a Liverpool docker, but do you know, if you want to go on the docks you've got to have your name down almost as soon as you are born!"

For some strange reason that remark stopped the conversation.

Research and Consultancy

94. Basil and the European Commission

In order to win research contracts from the European Commission, Basil Catachanas, a Belgian of Greek shipowning origins, needed someone from the UK and someone from France to make up his team. Through personal recommendations, he approached Mme Desautel Jamois from France and myself from the UK. Mme Desautel, a very clever economist, should have carried a health warning, as she went round in a permanent cloud of Gauloise cigarette smoke. We insisted she smoked only American cigarettes at work.

Brussels

We met in Brussels, put together a proposal, and won a contract to carry out research into harmonising Maritime Education and Training in Europe. We divided the work between us (I was allocated the UK, Eire and Denmark). We each went off, collected and analysed the data, and wrote up the conclusions. I sent my work to Basil and waited for three days to give him time to read it, then phoned.

Me: "Was the work I sent alright?"

Basil "I am very worried about your work!"

Me (on the defensive): "I have done exactly what we agreed!"

Basil (with a sigh): "Do you know how little we are being paid for this work?"

Me: "Yes. We deliberately reduced our rates in order to beat possible Italian and Spanish competitors"

Basil: "Correct! The stuff you have sent in is high quality work. You have given all the data and written it up so that it can be clearly understood. If we submit that sort of thing at the price, they will expect it all the time. What I want you to do is to miss out half the data and write it up in a confusing way. We will then submit it. They will say 'This is not good enough!' to which we will reply 'Well that is what you have paid us for, if you want a decent report, pay us some more money!"

While being devious with officials, Basil was very fair with me, and while we carried out this and other contracts, my bank balance never looked better.

I believe that one of the advantages of the EU is that we can learn things from other countries. I certainly learned a lot from Basil.

95. European Competitiveness

Invited by consultancy group TecnEcon to join them in bidding (successfully) for a contract with Directorate General VII (Transport) of the European Commission, I enjoyed the work, which was to try to make European shipping more competitive in the world market.

We looked at about 12 classes of ship in different trades. Whether we could suggest ways to make them more competitive depended on many things, size, building costs, manning policies, use of automation, etc. Some trades were already doing well, Liquefied Gas Tankers, Chemical Carriers, Container ships etc, but at the lower end of the scale, medium sized bulk carriers, which needed large crews to clean the holds and were affected by fickle charter rates, looked impossible. We recommended several ways to take those that were nearly competitive up above the "break-even" line, but recommended that the "hopeless cases" were left to the low-wage economies of the Far East.

The draft report was submitted and almost immediately we received angry phone calls saying, "This report is rubbish! Come to Brussels immediately!"

We duly obliged and were quickly told that we should have made the worst case ships – the medium sized dry bulkers – competitive. We said, in the current market, that is impossible. The official said "Nothing is impossible! How much subsidy would it require to make European dry bulkers competitive?" We said "Subsidies do not make ships competitive!" (We were from Mrs Thatcher's Enterprise Britain and subsidies did not figure in our thinking).

He explained: "I need to have evidence that European shipping is hopelessly uncompetitive and needs huge subsidies. I can then go to budget meetings alongside Agriculture, Rail and Road Transport etc and tell them I need a large slice of the budget, or my sector will be in real trouble! You have shown that we can mostly manage without subsidies at all. If I tell people that, I will get no money at all!"

What he wanted was a large budget to distribute. In his struggle with other departments, more money meant more power!

96. The Royal Navy's One Problem

My Master of Philosophy research project was about the navigational accuracy of merchant ships. Bearing in mind that the Royal Navy were plying the oceans ready to fire nuclear missiles, I thought they would already know accurately where they were, or at least would have the best scientists working with them to find out. The Admiralty's Navigational Research Centre was at the old Compass Observatory at Slough. They made me very welcome when I went to visit, they were proud of the new SINS (Ships'

Inertial Navigation Systems) and other scientific work. I explained what I was doing with regard to traditional, satellite and OMEGA merchant ship accuracy.

At the end of the meeting I asked "So what navigational problems does the Royal Navy have today?"

The senior scientist said "None!"

But a junior whispered "Ahem! We do have just the one, Sir!"

The senior repeated emphatically "None!"

I said "If you do have one problem, maybe we have it on merchant ships and I can help you?"

He said "You definitely do not have it on merchant ships!"

Me "What is it?"

Him: "It is Royal Navy Officers – they think they know where they are!"

He explained that they had sent a submarine to surface and rendezvous with a destroyer and they had each radioed in that they were at the exact rendezvous point, the visibility was eight miles and they could not see one another.

Many accidents to merchant ships happen when the navigators think they know where they are, and most groundings occur with the Echo Sounder switched off, because people thought they were in deep water.

97. Transfer of Technology

In 1986, I was very fortunate to be invited by the UK Government to lead a research project looking into the training needs for ships of the future. Part of the research was to visit other countries with "Future Ship" projects and share with them a vision of the future. In each country, the Foreign Office and Diplomatic Service pulled out all the stops so that we met the right researchers and project leaders. In Japan, Germany, Norway, we received translations of all their documents in advance and they received copies of our project description and questions in their own languages, in good time before we arrived. I discovered that embassy staff do a lot more than hold cocktail parties.

In Germany we met the leader of a project, already completed, to transfer advanced aircraft technology to future ships. We had a similar project starting in the UK. I said I thought the idea was very imaginative, and they said they thought so too! I asked "So, what did you learn from your project?"

The leader thought for a moment and then said "I think I can say honestly that we learned absolutely nothing!" When I asked why, he said that they had chosen Focker as the aircraft company and Krupp Atlas on the ship's equipment side. "Both are very competitive German industrial companies. So competitive, in fact, that they would not give away any of their secrets to anyone, so there was no transfer of technology at all!"

I reported this back to the UK Government Department and added "Surely the British are much better at teamwork than that!!" A thoughtful civil servant said that companies like Marconi and British Aerospace were not that good at exchanging secrets either, and told me to "watch this space", but not to hold my breath!

98. The Real World

I worked in the European Commission for nice people trying to help their industry sectors but largely out of touch with the "coal-face" and unaware of the difficulties which their new legislation created for those at the "sharp-end". I discovered that my role was to curb some of their exciting but crazy ideas. I remember being asked to implement a scheme, whereby every ship visiting Europe would be faced by an official, whose job was to assess the competency of the crew. My job was to be: To decide how the test would be carried out.

I pointed out some of the practical difficulties of such a scheme. Not all flag-of-convenience ships were sub-standard, not all seafarers from certain countries were incompetent, it takes time to carry out assessments etc etc.

I was in full flow when my host held up his hand and said "Stop! Stop! You are talking about the real world! We do not deal with the real world here!"

Later, a German official (an ex shipmaster) who shared my frustrations, arranged for me to lecture to about 100 bureaucrats about some of the practical consequences of new legislation. As they entered the room and were introduced, several said, "Pleased to meet you! We understand you are from the real world!"

99. It is an Unfair World

The Maritime Studies Department was asked to help two Biology research students who were studying the marine life that grows on the hulls of big tankers. One was very keen. He knew that the difference between a clean hull and a weedy one had a great effect on the speed of big tankers steaming from the Middle East to Europe. Trade was booming. Ships were not in port for very long and he would get up in the middle of the night and travel to Milford Haven to collect samples from the bottom of "his" ships. The other student was lazy. He couldn't be bothered to get up in the middle of the night. He heard that there were some ships laid up in a Loch in Scotland and he collected his samples from them – no need to worry about them sailing before he arrived. They were there for months (I think they included at least one new Gas Carrier waiting for appropriate terminals to be built).

When their theses were finished, the oil trade had slumped and the big tankers were slow-steaming round the Cape. No-one was interested in squeezing the last 0.1 knot from them. What people really wanted to know was how fast weed grew on laid-up tankers, so that they could judge what would be needed to re-commission them when trade improved.

You can guess whose thesis was in great demand! Life is not fair.

100. The New Job

Liverpool Polytechnic recruited a brilliant mathematician, a tall, imposing but impecunious young man who travelled by "folding" himself into a tiny Mini. Before joining us he had been carrying out very complicated abstract and intense research at a London University and his brain had become exhausted. The applied research, mathematically modelling the tension in mooring lines, which he did with us, was child's play to him and he relaxed and enjoyed it.

When it came time for him to leave, we wondered if he would return to the higher realms of academia, but were delighted when, after being interviewed in London, he came into college saying "Hey everyone! I am so lucky! I have got the job I really wanted! I am so happy!" We asked "What job is that Clive?" "I have got a job as a University Lecturer – it is what I really want to do"

We asked "Which University?"
He thought for a moment and said "Gabarone, I think!"

We asked "Where is that?"

He said "I don't know."

So we went off to get a world atlas and looked it up. It is in central southern Africa, in Botswana. He was surprised, but no less delighted with the new job. We wished him well and hope he enjoyed his new life.

101. Night Vision Devices

A young researcher from Liverpool University was looking into civilian uses for Night Vision devices developed for the military. He asked if we thought they could be used on merchant ships. Always interested in innovation, we arranged with Manchester Pilots to try out about several different models on the Manchester Ship Canal. A party of about six of us went to Eastham Lock to join the empty Manchester sludge barge (which had dumped treated sewage sludge in Liverpool Bay) on its return journey up the canal.

Incidentally, the Pilot Superintendent, seeing some of his pilots, on their day off, joining a ship which was exempt from pilotage, thought they had gone crazy and was about to send for the men with white coats, but we explained.

The devices varied in quality and type. Some worked on infra-red illumination, some used very highly amplified "stray light", some were like telescopes, some binoculars, some like spectacles. They had two main drawbacks. Night work on the bridge requires time for your eyes to become "dark-adapted" and every time you used a device, you lost your night vision for minutes afterwards. Secondly, the cascade amplifiers took time to process the light and if you accidentally looked at a shore light or other bright source, the image looked smoky for a long time before it cleared.

It was a very interesting exercise, and when we got off at Latchford Lock, one of the pilots said to the young researcher, "How much would the Barr and Stroud binocular device cost?" He replied that it would be well over a thousand pounds, but he was keen to learn "Do you think it would be useful to you in your job?" The pilot replied, "I don't think so. But I would really like a pair! I would be the best-equipped 'peeping tom' in the district!"

102. How to Identify a Tanker

The mathematical models which were developed at great expense by the National Physical Laboratory, to explain the drifting of broken down tankers, in some cases were not wholly convincing to us former seafarers. So we borrowed a model about five feet long and used a model tug "Kate" to do some experiments of manoeuvring a "dead" hull in high winds, on West Kirby Marine Lake.

The experiments were going well. We had attracted few onlookers because it was a cold and blustery day. One elderly couple were very interested. We caught this conversation:

Her, in a wobbly voice: "What sort of ship is that then, dear?"

Him, equally wobbly: "I don't know what it is, but I can tell you what it isn't!"

Her: "What isn't it?"

Him: "It isn't a tanker!"

Her: "How do you know that, dear?"

Him: "They don't paint them that colour!"

It was red.

103. Do Polytechnic Staff Offer Consultancy Services?

Do staff do consultancy?

At Liverpool Polytechnic, teaching was more important than research and consultancy. So when I received a telephone call at 11.15 a.m. one day the conversation went like this:

Caller: "Do Polytechnic staff offer consultancy services?"

Me: "Yes, they do"

Caller: "Is there anyone on the staff who could give advice on the stability of a damaged ship?"

Me; "Yes, there is. Dr Bryan Barrass, our Naval Architect"

Caller: "May I speak with him?"

Me: "Not right now, he is in the middle of a lecture to the BSc class. He will be available at 12 o'clock!"

Caller: "I need to speak to him now!!"

Me: "Sorry. What is the rush?"

Caller: "I am on a ship in the Gulf of Mexico and we are sinking, I need to speak to him NOW!"

Me: "In that case I will go and get him".

Bryan solved their problem and he so impressed them that the owner of the ship decided to send his son on our BSc course in the following year. We learned to our cost, that saving the ship was much easier than teaching the owner's son.

The Honourable Company of Master Mariners

104. The Honourable Company of Master Mariners

On 16th August 1953, I was invited by Captain Harold Redfearn, London Pilot, to visit HQS "Wellington" and become a cadet of the Honourable Company of Master Mariners. I knew very little about the Company.

On returning home my parents asked "What is the Honourable Company of Master Mariners?" I replied "It seems like a lot of funny old men in dressing gowns playing games!" My mother was still alive when I became a Warden and had my own robe/dressing gown.

I now know much more about Livery Companies and start my guided tours of the Wellington by saying "In the 1300 and 1400s the City of London had a terrible reputation for being full of rogues and thieves providing shoddy goods and services!" My audience sometimes says "Well! Not much change there, then!" That is unfair. The City decided to start Trade Guilds which would oversee each craft, make sure it was practised only by experienced Master Craftsmen and that all young people entering a profession would be apprenticed to a Master Craftsman. These Guilds became the Livery Companies of today. Their original aim was to raise standards and this tradition continues, with many Companies also providing educational and benevolent support to retired members of their profession.

The Master Mariners were not formed until 1926, when Sir Robert Burton Chadwick, MP for Wallasey and a shipowner and qualified Master Mariner, persuaded the City Chamberlain to help found the first new Livery Company (number 78) since the Fan Makers in the reign of Queen Anne more than 200 years before. The aim of the Company is "to encourage and maintain a high and honourable standard of ability and professional conduct in the officers of the British Merchant Navy".

The Master Mariners were the first "modern company". There are now more than 100 Livery Companies.

105. Reasons for Joining

The Honourable Company of Master Mariners Journal contained useful professional articles and the "Technical Extracts" were placed on board many merchant ships, including all of the Blue Funnel Line Fleet. I remember the Master on one of my ships coming up to me and saying "I understand you are an Apprentice of the Honourable Company of Master Mariners?" I replied that I was. He said "That is one organisation I regret not having joined!" When asked why he replied "It would have looked very good in my obituary".

There are other reasons for joining. In 2000, when I asked all the members in a questionnaire why they joined, they gave various reasons. Only one honest elderly member said, "I have forgotten!"

Activities today include supporting and enjoying:
- Professional activities, including advice and consultation for Government Departments and others, lectures and conferences
- Social events, meeting people (receptions, lunches, dinners etc)
- Livery Company activities in the City of London
- Charitable work, (Welfare, Education etc)
- Receiving publications – especially relevant to seagoing and overseas members
- Supporting new entrants and trainees

106. The Apprentices Committee

In the mid 1990s, with the UK fleet shrinking, the HCMM Apprentices scheme ground to a halt. When asked to restart it, I said "Only if the Employers will support it!" Most employers were keen, seeing it as a way of encouraging the professionalism and commitment of today's young people. So we restarted with one and have grown to more than 40 young people in the scheme.

We receive reports and visits from Masters and Mentors and from Apprentices and Junior Associates (those over 21) and we give advice and encouragement.

When one girl felt isolated and lonely on her first trip, her Master and I both told her we had had similar feelings, and

with Master and Apprentice

she stuck it out and is now doing well and is very happy.
Another young man spent his first three voyages on the
"Queen Elizabeth 2". We wrote saying he should ask his
company for a trip on a different sort of ship, because he
was not broadening his experience enough. He replied to
the contrary, he was broadening his experience a lot! He
later took our advice and did two trips on the "St Helena"
supplying the South Atlantic Islands, and wrote to us
saying he had gained more experience on that ship than on
most of his other voyages.

107. Giving Advice

If young people make the right career choices, it is usually
more by luck than good judgement. The best thing we
"oldies" can do, is set out all the facts and options and let
them make their own decisions.

Asking your employers for advice does not always work. They tell you what is best for them, not what is best for you, and the two things are not always the same. Having over 600 experienced members in branches of the marine industries, makes the Honourable Company a good source of advice for young people. Our members want the young people to be happy and make the most of their opportunities and the advice is honest and straightforward.

Bearing this in mind, I wrote to all the Apprentices and Junior Associates and said "In term of careers, we can advise on anything you may wish to do. Somewhere there will be a member who has trodden that path before, who will know the pros and cons of the decision you are about to make."

The first reply was from a young lady who had fallen in love with a marine engineer, and wanted advice. I searched for a member who had done that, and none came forward. Even if they had done so, they were not going to admit it. The advice required was whether shipping companies would allow a couple, a deck officer and an engineer, to sail together. Fortunately, I had come across the problem before, with a couple at Liverpool Polytechnic. Now, as then, I found three different policies. Some (like British Antarctic Survey) welcomed the idea. It added to the family atmosphere on board. The trouble was they were so happy, they stayed, so there were seldom any vacancies. Some had a definite policy forbidding it. Some companies had no policy and would consider what to do if the question arose. I cautioned that, in the Liverpool case, we had found that Esso Tankers were enthusiastic supporters of the idea.

The young couple joined and they were then sent, one to Japan and the other to Hamburg to join different ships. Supporting the policy did not mean they would carry it out!

108. The Bowler Hat

The Clerk told me, when I was Master of the Honourable Company, that I must be properly dressed when leading the wreath-laying party at the Merchant Navy Memorial Service at Tower Hill on Remembrance Day in November – and that included wearing a bowler hat.

Realising that you can get nearly anything on the Internet these days, I put "Bowler Hat" into the search engine and was overwhelmed with offers. The only problem was, they were plastic, in silver, gold, with Union Jacks, with starry spangles, etc etc No proper bowler hats.

Reverting to Gentlemen's Outfitters in the Yellow Pages, I found that the best shops in Northampton or Daventry no longer sold them, and they advised that I should go to London.   The first shop I tried in London was Harvey Nicholls – nothing! The next was Harrods. I went to the advice desk and asked for "Gentlemen's Outfitting?" The young Malaysian lad said "Sorry Sir, we do not have one" I said "I am sure you do!" He asked "What do you want?" When I told him a bowler hat, he smiled and said "Bowler Hat, Sir, No problem at all! You should have said straight away! Bowler hats – Sports Department, straight ahead down there!"

At that point I saw the Gents Outfitting off to the left, thanked the chap and made off to the left. He rushed from behind his desk and steered me back towards the Sports Department. After a short struggle he gave up.

On approaching Gents Outfitting, a young assistant asked what I wanted. I said "A Bowler Hat. It will need to be a big one – I think my head is size seven and a quarter!" An elderly assistant behind him said "Seven and a quarter, I don't think so, Sir, you look like a seven and three eights to me!" Sure enough he was right and in a few minutes he brought one from the basement and I walked off with a Bowler that fitted perfectly and my wallet lighter by £129!

109. Saxmundham

The Clerk advised that, as Master of the Company, I should not take foreign holidays during my year of office, as I might be required urgently for meetings in London. Bearing this in mind, we booked a holiday cottage in Westleton, near Aldeburgh, Suffolk. Sure enough, in the middle of August, I was asked to go to London for a meeting. I went to the tiny station at Saxmundham and asked for the train times next day, to get me to London for a meeting at 11 a.m.. The old man in the ticket office thought for a long time and then, in a beautiful slow Suffolk accent said "Oi can arffer you two trains in the mornin' Sir. First, there is the 8.30. That'll get you there in good time." He then thought a bit more, and added, "Then there's the other one, but that'll get you there too late!"

110. Livery Companies – an interesting life?

HQS Wellington

As Master of the Honourable Company you represent your profession at meetings and events in the City of London and elsewhere. Being introduced to members of other Livery Companies is fascinating, because these are people from other walks of life, that you would not normally meet. Being recognised by the Lord Mayor, Sheriffs, Lords, Judges and even members of the Royal family, was a novel experience for me – and also for Ann.

Most were friendly and open, even the Masters and Prime Wardens of the "Great Twelve" Livery Companies. During my year, Mr Blair and his Government were trying to stop the Livery Companies using their funds to help schools and colleges. They wanted to have access to, and spend, the money themselves. The real benefit of the Liveries, was that the (approximately) £32 million each year which they spent on good causes, was not just money, it came with the free help and support of generous, experienced and dedicated professional people.

Most people recognised and appreciated that the Master Mariners (and the Merchants / Traders) had helped to found the commercial wealth of the City from the Middle Ages to the present day. I tried to discover whether other people had maritime connections. I remember one conversation very clearly. I sat next to an elderly gentleman and asked him whether he had had an interesting life and whether he had any connections with the sea. He said, "My life has been very boring. It all started with the misfortune of being born into the wrong family. You see, my father was very rich – and my uncle was even richer. When I was about seven they said to me 'My boy, we think you should become a banker!' So I became a banker and it was boring! Connections with the sea – funny you should ask - because the answer is 'No!' It could have been 'Yes!', because a lot of people came to me and asked me to buy shipping companies, but I knew only what I saw on TV – they have accidents and spill oil, so I said 'No, Thank You!'

An interesting contrast to Greek shipowners I met – they sent one son into a bank and another into their own shipping company, so when they wanted to borrow money for a new ship, they had no problems at all.

111. The Mercers' Cup

When I became Master of the Honourable Company of Master Mariners I was given some valuable advice. One of my predecessors told me that, in his year of office, a valuable cup was stolen from a display case (they are now well secured). The cup had been given to the Master Mariners by the Worshipful Company of Mercers, one of the "great twelve" senior Livery Companies. Its loss was very embarrassing, especially as the Master Mercer would be dining on the "Wellington" in the near future. Our Master said "I would do anything to get the cup back!" The detective on the case said "That's no good! Do nothing!" Days went past and eventually a note was received from the detective, telling the Master to go to a particular stall in Stepney Market with a pocket full of "tenners", and ask "Have you got any cups?". He did as he was advised, the cup was produced from under the counter, the money paid and everyone was happy.

When asked to explain what was going on, the detective said "If you had done anything – announced it was stolen or made any other move – the thieves would have thrown it in the river or melted it down. We had an idea who might have stolen it, and where they might try to sell it. You got it back, didn't you!"

The claim on insurance had to be withdrawn. But the Master said wistfully "I didn't get my tenners back!"

112. Not what they seem...

"When you meet people from other Livery Companies, take care, don't jump to conclusions!" I was advised.

A Past Master told me that his first official function as Master was a dinner with the Worshipful Company of Fan Makers.

Thinking, they only made genteel ladies fans, he said rather disparagingly to his neighbour at dinner "And what sort of fans do you make?" His host said "I designed the RB211 jet engine for Rolls Royce!" The Fan Makers today include modern electric fans and jet engines in their sphere of interest.

Many of the older Livery Companies, such as the Fletchers (Arrow Makers) and Bowyers (Bow Makers), who may seem out of date in modern society, do wonderful work for charity and sports, including support for paraplegic games.

113. Livery Company Recruitment

Sitting next to the Master of the Worshipful Company of Water Conservators at dinner, I asked about his life's work.

"Well!" he said "At the age of 16, I started working in sewers. I have just retired at the age of 65, and thinking about it, I have spent my whole life in sewers".

I replied "The Master Mariners thought they had an image problem, but it must pale into insignificance when compared with yours! Does your industry have a problem recruiting?"

"Funny you should say that. Yes!"

He said that many of their members rise to very important positions in the major water companies in the UK and abroad, such as managing director of Anglian or Severn

Trent Water Companies or managers of huge irrigation projects overseas. Important, well paid and well respected positions.

To communicate with young people, they put career profiles of some of their successful members on the industry's recruitment web sites, and waited for the applications to flood in. I asked if the strategy had worked, to which he replied "No difference at all, still very few applicants, of a poor standard".

Incidentally, I had been to a Merchant Navy cadet recruitment day some years before and asked BP Tanker recruiters if they told potential recruits that their managing director had started as a cadet at sea. "Good Lord! No!" They said, "They would all want to be managing directors!"

Returning to the Water Conservators. Their next move was to look round their industry to find people who were in their early 20s, who really enjoyed their work. Instead of successful older people, they focussed their next advertising/internet features on these young people. There was an immediate rapport with potential applicants. The number and quality of recruits immediately improved.

The lesson from this, is that people in their fifties and sixties are not seen as role models for school leavers. The younger the role model, the better the links. Hence, it is often the cadets and third mates, if they are enjoying their jobs at sea, who can influence young people to join the Merchant Navy.

St Lawrence and the Great Lakes

114. Manchester Liners

Meeting Lakers

In 1968, as a lecturer, I was returning to sea for a voyage to do some research and gather new lecture material. Walking along the quayside in Salford Docks to join the "Manchester Port", I was surprised to see that the stem plate (bow) was very bent and buckled. At dinner, I mentioned this to the ship's other officers and they said, "Did you look at the other two ships as you walked past? Manchester Liners are all the same!" Apparently, the St Lawrence Seaway had not long been opened and the Great Lakes pilots were not used to handling the ocean-going ships now trading into the centre of Canada and the United States. Someone who could handle a "Laker" could not necessarily handle an ocean going ship of similar size. Lake ships have their bridges right forward and the deep-sea ships have them down aft – the pilots made a lot of mistakes in the early days.

115. Bosun and double beds

Whilst in a Canadian port, we heard an overseas Merchant Navy programme from the UK about the new ships being introduced by Manchester Liners for the Great Lakes trade. I was standing next to the Bosun, outside the Crews' Messroom, listening to the broadcast. When it got to the point of describing the accommodation, they said "And on these new ships, even the Petty Officers will be able to take their wives!". The salty old Bosun nearly exploded. "Bloody hell!" He said "Whatever next! If she's coming, I'm not!"

116. TV on the bow

In Manchester Docks, the Superintendent proudly described to visitors to the new "Manchester Port" a TV camera at the top of the foremast, pointing down towards the bow of the ship". He said how difficult it was to see from the bridge, the small ships sharing Seaway Locks with them, so they needed that device to see when it was clear ahead to leave the lock.

In Montreal we had visitors again and the same story was told to the visiting News Media. Everyone was impressed, including me. I was surprised therefore, when the Mate ordered the Bosun to dismantle and stow the camera as we left to go through the Seaway. I asked innocently why it was being dismantled, just when it was most needed. The Mate said "It might get damaged or stolen. The camera is really just for showing to visitors!" I asked "How do you see when the small ships are clear from under the bow?" He said "There is a fellow who stands on the side of the lock, who gives us a thumbs up sign and shouts 'OK! All clear!'"

So much for the wonders of new technology.

117. Pumping the Bilges

"Manchester Port" was a highly automated ship – the first of a new era. All sorts of operations could be carried out, simply by pushing buttons on the bridge. Rumour has it that one of the office girls who enjoyed too many glasses of champagne at the ship's christening party in Manchester, had collapsed forward onto the array of lights and buttons and started pumps and opened valves with various parts of her anatomy. Be that as it may, visitors to the new ship were very impressed!

Having seen all this exciting new "kit," I asked if I could do a trip to Canada and the company agreed. On our first morning in the open sea, the Ship's Carpenter came to find me and said, "Would you like to see me pump the bilges?" He was in a smart white boiler suit and we proceeded to the bridge, where he pushed two buttons to open valves and another one to start the bilge pump. He then ran off the bridge at high speed. It seemed ages before he returned, filthy, wet and sweating, to press the next buttons.

Naturally I said "Where have you been?"
He explained "You saw me press these buttons to open the valves?"

Me "Yes! And a light came on to show you that the valve was open!"

"Wrong!" He said "That light only tells me I have just pressed a button. If I want to know whether the valve is open, I have to run down to the Engineroom and crawl through the Duct Keel up to No 1 hatch, and feel if it is open."

In the old days the pipes were run through the Duct Keel to the Engineroom and were easily accessible. On the "automated" ships they left the valves at each hatch. At sea, the Duct Keel often had some bilge water in it and as you crawled along, if the ship pitched, you were met by a wall of dirty water rushing over you.

So what impressed people in Manchester, did not help crewmembers very much at sea!

118. The Welland Canal

As the "Manchester Port" came back through the Welland Canal towards Lake Erie, I had asked to be called early in the morning. I was going to visit a friend at the college in Welland, where they had a new Navigational Aids simulator. At one point, at about 6 am, the ship had tied up to the canal bank, and they put a ladder over for me to go ashore to a phone box, to call my friend. My friends were a bit slow answering and as I looked out of the call box, the ship was moving off. The officers cheerfully waved and said, "You didn't want to come back on board did you?" I said no. I had not a clue where I was, but walked along the canal bank until I came to a small town. By this time the shops were open, and I found a travel agent. "Good morning, Sir, and where would you like to travel to?" I replied "Let us start at the beginning, where am I?" I caught a bus to Welland and had an interesting day.

Through the bridges

We visited the Welland Control Centre at Thorold and were shown their array of new equipment. I had noticed that each bridge on the canal had its own radar. "Do you guide the ships through I foggy weather?" I asked.

"No" They replied "The sole purpose of the radar is to give us time to get the bridge out of the way before a ship arrives." Logical.

The Thorold Centre had an amazing closed circuit TV system. They could zoom in to see minute details on the ships. I asked " What do you use it for?" They said, "It is a bit useless really, because when we really need to see things, in fog and at night, you cannot see much with a normal TV camera!" One operator had found a good use for it. He discovered that scantily clad Swedish stewardesses sunbathed on the monkey island on hot summer days and he was selling videos of them at a good price. Such enterprise was frowned upon and he was sacked, so the TVs went back to being almost useless.

119. A Canadian View of the English

Travelling by Intercity Bus from Toronto to Ottawa to see my cousin Betty and her policeman husband Wilf, I wanted to see the scenery, so sat at the front near the driver. We stopped half way at a café and I was first to the counter.

Middle aged lady serving at counter "What do want?"

Me: "Coffee, please!"

Lady: "What sort of coffee?"

Me: "White, please"

Lady "What do you mean 'white'?"

Me: "Not black coffee, white coffee, please"

Lady (at top of her voice to everyone in the café: "Listen everybody! We got some sort of RACIALIST here! He is asking for WHITE coffee!"

Lady, quietly to me "Do you want it with cream or without?"

Me: "With, please! I am sorry, but we call that white coffee in England!"

Lady "I was in England during the war, and they never said such rude things then!"

Returning from Ottawa I sat in the front seat again, and a young Canadian man sat next to me. Without my saying a word he asked "You are English, aren't you?" I said I was and asked him how he knew. He replied "Englishmen don't press their suits!" Looking down, I realised that a few days travelling had caused the creases to be less than perfect. Perhaps he had a point. He had taught me a lesson!

120. Accurate Time of Arrival

Leaving Detroit for Chicago, the ship radioed the US Coastguard and said "We'll be arriving at Chicago some time on Sunday afternoon." The young and rather officious Coastguard Vessel Traffic Service operator said "I am sorry Sir, but that is just not accurate enough!" The Chief Officer, knowing he could not judge the Estimated Time of Arrival within even an hour or two said "We shall be arriving on Sunday at 14 hours 32 minutes and 15 seconds!" Without a hint of amusement the Coastguard man said "That's better Sir, Why didn't you say that in the first place?" This told us that the VTS operator knew nothing about the navigational problems of the ships he was supposed to be serving.

When a new Secretary General was appointed at the International Maritime Organization, I sat next to him at dinner at the Institute of Marine Engineers. I used the above story to illustrate how seafarers lose respect for people who clearly have no concept of the difficulty of the work they do. I asked where the new SG had worked before joining IMO. "The St Lawrence Seaway" he said – it was Bill O'Neil. I had put my foot right in it! However, Bill went on to earn the respect of all seafarers in his work at IMO, helping to make ships safer and the seas cleaner, and is now a firm personal friend.

121. Cork

On the homeward voyage "Manchester Port" called at Cork in Southern Ireland to discharge grain loaded in Chicago. In order to get to the grain in the lower holds, several containers had to be lifted onto the deck. On arrival, the grain berth was occupied and we tied up alongside a main road, south of the city, to wait our turn.

In mid afternoon an old man came slowly up the gangway. He said that he wanted to see the man in charge. The Second Mate explained he was on duty. The old man said "But you are not really in charge!"

Second Mate: "The previous few days have been foggy and the Master is resting. You tell me what you want, and I will call the Master if it is important enough."

Old Man: "I see you have just arrived with a load of bungalows and I would like to buy one! The reason I want to talk to the man in charge, is that I don't want to pay my money to a subordinate and then find he was not entitled to sell the thing to me."

The fact that the containers had no windows did not seem to worry him. But then, I am told hundred of containers go missing every day, and many jungle clearings in Africa have families living in them.

Holidays and Travel

122. North Sea Ferries

Liverpool Polytechnic travelling expenses were not generous. Several members of staff travelling to conferences had gone hungry. I was travelling to Rotterdam on North Sea ferries, to arrange a joint conference with the University of Delft. I was hungry, and the other passengers were tucking-in to a wonderful buffet, I watched from the outside deck, feeling miserable and hungry. It was not until I spoke to other passengers later, that I realised the buffet was included in the fare. That made me feel even worse!

As we neared port, I realised time was going to be tight. The Hull to Rotterdam Ferry does not go to Rotterdam at all, but to a remote berth in Europort. Fortunately I got talking to a couple, who had been on holiday in Scotland. He was a former Dutch Air Force pilot who had married a Scots girl during the war, and after the war had gone on to found a successful airline - Martin Air. They were in a sports car and were going to Delft. They would take me, if I did not mind sitting in the small seat in the back on their luggage. I readily agreed. We went through the customs shed in the car and were stopped and questioned by an official. After a brief discussion in Dutch he let us proceed. As we drove out of the docks the driver said to me "Phew! That was close! He would not have been very pleased if he had known what you are sitting on!" I did not ask! They took me to Delft and I got to my meeting in good time.

123. The Money Belt

On a London Routemaster bus, we stopped in Oxford Street and a man got off and walked down a side street. Suddenly, the young black conductress jumped off and chased after him down the street. The Routemasters (and conductors/conductresses) were about to be phased out and I had seen many of the staff not bothering much to collect fares. I had never seen such enthusiasm and dedication! She dragged the man back to the bus, took him to his seat, pointed, and said "Is that yours?" It was a money belt. He said "Thank you very much. It was a bit tight and when I sat down I loosened it. I am so grateful to you!" She then took on the appearance of a strict "schoolmarm." She shook her finger at him and said "If I had not caught you, I would have had trouble, having to fill in forms, you would have had problems all day without your money! Don't you ever do that again!" He stood there like a guilty schoolboy!

124. The Bishop of Birkenhead

With Marine Engineering colleague, Eric Knowles, I was going from Euston to Lambeth for a Nautical Institute meeting. We were seated at the back, on the nearly-empty top deck of a bus. Sitting across the front seats were several bishops, obviously going to Lambeth Palace, home of the Archbishop of Canterbury.

I said to Eric "Did you see there were loads of Clerics on the train this morning?". "Yes!" he replied. He went on to say that, although he was a regular churchgoer in the Birkenhead Diocese, he would not recognise the

Bishop of Birkenhead if he tripped over him. At that, one of the bishops on the front row turned round and said "Did someone mention my name?" We said "Yes" and apologised. We then had a very interesting discussion with them for the rest of the trip.

125. Loch Lomond

When my ship visited Glasgow on one occasion, I was invited to see the beautiful scenery around Loch Lomond

Loch Lomond

by the family of Bill Lillie, my good friend from our days as midshipmen. Bill's father was a strict disciplinarian and was very well respected by everyone, including his family. As we were leaving Loch Lomond, we came to a road junction with a new roundabout. Bill's father indicated to turn right, drove the car up the kerb, through the flower beds on the roundabout and off down the side road. No one said anything for ages until a very thoughtful Mr Lillie senior said "That was nay there last time I came!"

126. Seat Belts

Ford Anglia

My ship was in Glasgow. I was a junior officer and I was pleased to get a call from my friend Bill Lillie. He had just bought a new car – Ford's revolutionary (then) "light" car - a Ford Anglia. Bill drove down to the ship to take me for a trial drive. He was proud of his new car, but doubtful of the value of the new-fangled devices the salesman had persuaded him to buy – seat belts. Bill, a canny Scot, mused "I suppose I was right to get the seat belts, but the trouble is, unless you have a crash, they are a waste of money!" We then drove off around the hills and lochs at break-neck speed and went off the road a couple of times, just to prove Bill had not wasted his money.

127. Subic Bay

Many years after visiting the Philippines as a ship's officer, I returned to represent Videotel at conferences and meetings. One conference included a visit to the former US Naval Base at Subic Bay – being redeveloped as an industrial and commercial centre. The conference had several hundred delegates. We arrived at Manila airport to fly to Subic. We were surprised and a bit alarmed to see the old aeroplanes that had been chartered for the flight. I was in the first plane. We took off and rattled our way over the mountain and landed safely at Subic Bay. We were told that the second plane was following fifteen minutes behind us and we should await their arrival. 20 minutes went by – no plane – 30 minutes – 40 minutes – still no plane. We were preparing for bad news. There was then a drone of engines and the plane appeared over the hill and landed safety.

The obvious question: "Where have you been, we were worried about you?"

They explained, "Well, it was like this. We took off 15 minutes after you. When we were up, someone said to the aircrew 'Isn't there a volcano erupting somewhere near here?' The crew said 'Yes. Mount Pinotubo, in the north. Would you like to see it?' We said yes, and they took us to see it. We flew around the volcanic cloud – very interesting!"

Flying back to Manila, we took a route along the coast flying low past the islands, bays and beaches. We asked the stewardess "Has the pilot chosen the scenic route just for us?" "No" she said, "The door would not shut properly, so we couldn't pressurise the plane and have had to keep at a low altitude!"

128. Taxis

For a while, the Worshipful Company of Hackney Carriage Drivers – the Livery Company of taxi drivers – had their offices on board HQS "Wellington". I would tell visitors to the ship how lucky we are to have proper licensed cabs in London. They all have to learn "The Knowledge" including every street and all major venues in the City, including all 38 Livery Company halls – they know their stuff. I used to compare them with Copenhagen. When I went there, I was told that the taxi drivers were Balkan asylum seekers, they spoke no Danish, very little English, did not know the City and charged extortionate fares, so you should agree the fare before you set off, have your own road map and know the route. Copenhagen turned out to be that bad in practice, but I was prepared.

My illusions about London were shattered when I was Master of the Honourable Company and due at an official lunch in the Painter-Stainers Hall in Little Trinity Lane. My driver said "I think I know where Little Trinity Lane is, and drove off towards Trinity House at Tower Hill. I said "This is the wrong way. You should know all the Livery Halls – you learned them when you were doing 'The Knowledge'!" "Yes, he said, "But that was more than 20 years ago, and I have forgotten!" We finished up with me on my mobile phone and Ann on hers in our flat, holding an A-Z of London, directing us to the Hall!

I arrived late and my faith in the system was somewhat dented!

129. Mobile Phones

In the early days of mobile phones, few people had them. The few who had, liked to show off on the train by sitting up high and announcing loudly to their callers "I am on the train....etc.!!" The only satisfaction other travellers had, was when you went into a tunnel, the man lost his connection and was left saying "Hello! Hello! Hello!... " to a dead phone and sank shame-faced down further into his seat. It made the rest of us smile.

On a train to Newcastle upon Tyne, the chap opposite me spent most of the journey calling people and saying "Yes I'll have a million!" or two million, or even 10 million. I thought he must be very rich. We got talking later. He was an ordinary man, in an ordinary job, ordering leaflets from printers for Government Departments.

Again on the Newcastle train. A fresh-faced lad joined the train in Manchester. He was smartly dressed and I immediately summed up the situation. He was a sixth-former going for interview at University. We were at Miles Platting, just outside Manchester, when a phone went off in his holdall. He answered it "Yes mother, I am alright!" We reached Huddersfield when the phone went again "Yes mother, I am still alright!" When we reached York it went again. "Yes mother, I am still, still alright!" He switched it off.

I don't blame him!

130. Getting in to Australia

I left my passport at Australia House in London, to get a visa put into it for a trip "down under". I then needed to retrieve it urgently for a trip to Spain. I was standing in the queue when I overheard an interesting dialogue between the woman in front of me and the clerk behind the desk.

Clerk: "…and how long did you stay in Australia on your temporary visa last time?"

Her: "Seven years"

Clerk: "Seven years on a temporary visa is way too long. …. And I understand you were deported?"

Her (very indignant): "I was not! I was not deported! I was thrown out!"

There was then a debate about whether she was told to leave and went peacefully or whether she had been physically picked up, taken to the airport and put on a plane. Apparently "Deported" and "Thrown out" are not the same in immigration terms.

Clerk: "I am not sure if I can give you a visa!"

Her: "Well I am going anyway, to marry my fiancé!"

Clerk: "Well why didn't you say that in the first place! You're in the wrong queue, you should be over there!"

131. Belfast Hospitality

I was Chairman of the Association of Navigation Schools when the time came to have the AGM in Belfast, in the middle of "the troubles" (the sectarian confrontation between Protestants and Roman Catholics). The people of Belfast made us very welcome.

We stayed at the University and on the first evening we were all taken to the Ulster Folk and Transport Museum. The forecast said rain, but when we got to the destination the weather had cleared, so I said to the coach driver "Is it OK if I leave my raincoat on the rack?" "Certainly, Sir, No problem at all, it will be fine!"

At the end of the evening, I got on the coach and the raincoat was missing.

I asked "Do you know where my raincoat is?"

Him: "I have no idea!"

Me: "You said I could leave it and it would be alright!"

Him: "I don't know about that! After taking you I did trips with two other groups, I can't be responsible for your coat".

I thought, "Well, thanks a lot!"

As we got off the coach he said:

"I think I know what might have happened to your coat. During the evening the first bus broke down and I changed to another one!"

Next day we passed the first bus in the middle of the street and the two buses stopped in the middle of the traffic while the other driver explained that he had found the coat and had put it in a locker at the depot.

The coat was sent back three weeks later by post, because the man with the locker key had been on holiday!

132. The Silverlink Train Time Mystery

In past years Silverlink never had leaflets ready when the timetables changed from summer to winter or vice versa. In winter 2006, they did. However, I noticed that the leaflets bore little resemblance to the departure times on the board, so I asked the young man at the information desk. The conversation went like this:

Me: "This leaflet bears very little resemblance to the times on the board"

Him: "Funny you should say that, because trains keep appearing on my computer screen when I am not expecting them!"

I showed him my leaflet valid 13th December 2005 to 9th June 2006.

Him: "Your problem is that you have the Milton Keynes to London leaflet!"

Me: "That is because I want to travel between Milton Keynes and London"

Him: "I think it was printed early, before they finalised the timetable".

Me: "Oh, I see!"

Him: (reaching into a secret store under his desk): "I have a timetable here which gives the correct times, would you like one?"

So I now know when the trains actually run. I suppose if you have printed thousands of leaflets you have to get rid of them somehow. I hope next time they will get it right.

133. A Taller Story

Queenstown in South Island New Zealand is a beautiful town. The young residents thought is was a bit boring, so New Zealand's entrepreneur A J Hackett invented the first of the many "extreme sports" now available in the region – bungy jumping. It is described as "the ultimate adrenalin rush".

Ann and I thought we were a bit old for it, but we were intrigued by the following conversation overheard at breakfast:

Waitress, proudly, in an attractive Eastern European accent: "My boyfriend did three bungy jumps, one after the other, yesterday!"

Guest "Did it make him taller?"

Waitress "I really hope so! You see, he is too short for me!"

Cultural Exchanges

134. Alexandria

A lecturer in Egypt

I had not been to Alexandria before. One of my colleagues at Liverpool Polytechnic had been asked to run staff seminars at the Arab Maritime Transport Academy in Alexandria before me. He told me two golden rules. Samir Mankabady had been born in Egypt when King Farouk was on the throne and his family had to leave when Colonel Nasser took over, so spoke Arabic and knew the country well. He said that despite having been brought up on Egyptian food, he survived only one or two days before getting terrible tummy trouble. Golden Rule Number 1 was "Mind what you eat. Each lecturer will invite you to his home and will try to outdo the others with the lavish spread he offers you". The Second Golden Rule was "The flights from the UK arrive in the early evening and the desert road to Alex is a death trap after dark, so insist on staying in Cairo overnight".

I spent the flight chatting to Commodore Ibrahim Hussein, who had been studying in Liverpool. As we touched down, he said "I am going straight home to Alexandria when we land". I said, "I am staying in Cairo", to which he replied "Oh! I took the liberty of cancelling your room, so you could travel with me". We took the Delta Road, half the drivers were drugged to keep themselves awake, it was foggy and each time the road dipped to cross a bridge over a "wadi", the visibility was zero. You could hear the odd creaky cart and donkey, but could not see anything! It was a nightmare ride.

I failed on the other "Golden Rule" too. My stomach arrived home about three days after I did!

135. The International Job

The dining car on the old British Rail service between Liverpool and London was an interesting place to meet people. You could buy a Second Class ticket and dine with First Class passengers. One evening I had dinner with a top executive of Wimpey, the construction group. He told me that he had been Head of Wimpey UK, and knew that, in terms of seniority and experience, he might be selected as Head of Wimpey International. He said "I explained to the Chairman, that I hate flying, and so did not wish to be considered for the international job. The Chairman thanked me and took note of my request. Imagine how I felt when, without consulting me, it was announced that I was the new Head of Wimpey International! I went straight to the Chairman and said 'What is going on? Did you forget my request?'. 'No' said the Chairman, 'I remembered it well. You see, we have a lot of young executives in this organisation who are only too happy to jump on a plane at the drop of a hat, fly round the world and spend a long time living in luxury hotels. At least I will know, that if you have to go, it will be absolutely necessary!'"

Shrewd personnel management or nasty meanness?

136. Students from Algiers

Liverpool Polytechnic was asked to take second year University students from Algeria and put them through a full four year Nautical degree programme, so that they could become Harbour Masters, Maritime Administrators etc. They spoke only French and Arabic and so were sent to an English language course in Essex in January, prior to joining us in September. I made the mistake of inviting them for interview when they had only had a month in Colchester.

My French is weak and their English equally so, so it was a struggle. We did quite well in establishing their level of Mathematics and Science, because they had a French-style Baccalaureate. When It came to English I asked the first applicant "Which English books have you read?" Looking very embarrassed, he said "It does not matter!" "Oh yes, it does matter" I said, "If you do not tell me which English books you have read, you cannot come on the BSc course" Very shyly, he said "I have just finished ze one about ze Fox, ze Duck and ze little chicken!" I recognised the book I read to my grandchildren: "Chicken Licken". That made me realise how poor the range of books was, for adults learning English for the first time, and my mistake for not inviting them to come for interview much later.

I asked if they wanted to ask me any questions. They asked "What language do they speak in Colchester?" I told them it was English. They said definitely not. They spoke English in the school, but in the town everyone used a different language. I said "You mean, in the school, you say 'Good Morning' to someone, they say 'Good Morning' to you, but in the town, if you say 'Good Morning' they reply 'Owse it goin then boor!'" Their eyes lit up – "Yes, that is right – what language is that?" I had to explain that it was a special Colchester/Essex version of English. They did not understand.

137. What is History?

The Arab Maritime Transport Academy in Alexandria invited me to visit, mainly to up-date the lecturers on recent research and teaching. I was made very welcome and shown round. In the market place (the souk), at first I had my guide nearly in tears, I was so poor at bargaining. I either accepted too high a price or offered so little it insulted the storekeeper. I got better at it and was eventually certified as a haggler of Egyptian standard.

One visit was to the new museum in Alexandria, which told stories of Egyptian history. I had been brought up on British school history. I knew that the Crusaders were the "good guys" and that Saladdin and his Moslem warriors were the "bad guys". I also vaguely remembered that the crusaders always won. Not in Egyptian history! The tableaux and paintings all showed triumphant and heroic moslem warriors giving the crusaders a "hell of a beating!" Coming to modern times I thought Israel had won the 6-day Arab-Israeli war in 1967. Not in Arab history. The Arabs apparently sank one Israeli gunboat. Nearly all the exhibits showed that event. There were pictures of it from every angle, models of it, souvenirs from the attack etc.

I realised that each nation's history is seen from a different viewpoint.

138. Discipline in the Philippines

I was President of the Nautical Institute. After inaugurating the Philippines Branch in Manila we had dinner in the hotel with local members and their friends. The discussion was interrupted when a senior European Manager said to the Filipino shipmaster by his side:

"The trouble with you chaps is that you cannot administer discipline!"

The Filipino Master was most hurt.

"Sir!" he said " You know that is just not true. Don't you remember that last voyage I was having trouble with my Second Mate. I followed the company disciplinary procedures TO THE LETTER!"

"Yes I remember and you are quite right, you followed the

company disciplinary procedures TO THE LETTER. You only missed out on one thing!"

"What was that?"

"You didn't tell the man he was being disciplined!"

"I couldn't, he is my friend!"

It gives an insight into the way Filipino Masters work with their crews. They wish to be respected and liked, so that in a crisis, the crew members will go beyond the normal course of duty to support them.

The " I give the orders, and you obey" culture of our Royal Navy would not work.

139. By the Book

Charles Cotter wrote books on navigation. He was a clever man and worked hard, but he was not very good at proof reading. This came to the fore when the ship I was serving in called at Singapore and Chinese Cadet Goh Choo Keng joined us, and was told to keep the 8-12 watch with me.

I helped him with his studies. One evening he came to me with a question from Charles Cotter's book. "I have worked it out three times. I get the same answer each time, and it does not agree with the answer in the book". I worked it out and agreed with him. I knew Charles Cotter's book. I said to Cadet Goh "You are right, the book is wrong! Don't worry about it any more!"

I was surprised at breakfast next morning to find Goh with bags under his eyes looking as if he had been up all night.

He had! "I still can't get the right answer!" he said. I told him he had had the right answer the night before. The book was wrong. "No, no" he said "The book cannot be wrong!"

More than 25 years later, Captain Goh, who was by now a venerable and respected former Singapore Harbour Master and Director of Marine, was entertaining Ann and I to dinner at the Keppel Club. He reminded me of our first watch together. The ship was sailing east towards the Horsburgh Light and the South China Sea and there were heavy showers about. I was in the wheelhouse and he was keeping lookout on the wing of the bridge. He came to the wheelhouse door and asked "Please Sir, can I go below and get my raincoat?" Apparently I said "No. You just stay there and get wet. That will remind you to bring it with you next time. When you are Third Mate you will not be allowed to leave the bridge!" I did not know I had ever been THAT mean! I had forgotten the incident. He hadn't!

140. China

Holt's Wharf, Kowloon was Blue Funnel Line's major base in Hong Kong. They employed huge numbers of Chinese workers, (many of whom were refugees from Communist China). When the ships were Northbound, they would chip off any rust spots on the black hull and paint them with bright red-lead paint. The ships used to go north looking as if they had measles. On return from the north, the painters put on the black topcoat and the ships returned to Europe gleaming.

When Chairman Mao and the Red Army took control in China, they had initiated various five-year plans. They were short of iron and steel, so Mao declared that every citizen should have a blast furnace in his or her backyard. His word was law. They did it. However, most of the iron

At Holt's Wharf Kowloon

they produced was of very poor quality, full of impurities. It cracked and crumbled. They needed railway wagon wheels. Our ship was in Hong Kong, about to sail for Shanghai, with a cargo that included a large number of railway wheels from Europe.

We had an urgent message from Liverpool Headquarters "The previous ship had steamed up the Yangtze River and arrived in Shanghai to an enormous problem with the authorities. Unknown to the ship's staff, some disaffected painters in Hong Kong had joined up the dots of red-lead on the ship's side to form Chinese characters that said something very rude about Chairman Mao. All future ships must be searched inside and out for anything which looked like Chinese characters"

Amongst the areas I searched was the Engineroom. I was accompanied by our senior Chinese Rating, No 1 Fireman. I was surprised to find a huge painted sign in Chinese, from top to bottom on one side of the Engineroom.

Me: "What does that sign say?"

No 1 Fireman: "It does not matter!"

Me: "Oh yes it does! What does it say?"

No 1: "Sign not say anything about Mao Tse Tung!"

Me: "Maybe not, but what does it say?"

No 1 (very embarrassed): "It say Chief Engineer's mother and father not properly married!"

141. An American View of Failure

I had been invited by the Hydrographer of the Navy to give a paper at a large Oceanology Conference in Brighton, saying how poor and out of date Admiralty charts were at that time. I was happy to do that because I saw the dangers of surveyors thinking the surveys were too few and too old, and shipmasters believing the charts implicitly (they had to, they had nothing else). One or two people thought

I was rude to say those things with the Hydrographer (David Haslam) sitting in the front row.

About a year later, I saw David in London and he said cheerfully "Our strategy worked!" I said "I did not know we had a strategy!" His budget for surveying had been increased by many millions of pounds because someone from outside his department had criticised (justly) the limited scope of modern surveys.

At breakfast during the conference I was very pleased to talk to an American delegate who had been part of the research team developing satellite navigation systems at John Hopkins University. I had read the history of the Transit/Navy Navigation Satellite System when writing my chapter in Commander May's book "A History of Navigation". Reading it in a book was nowhere near as good as meeting someone who had been part of it. I said how much I admired Richard Kershner, who devised and launched the first US navigation satellite. It flew for only about 9 seconds before the rocket crashed into the ocean with its valuable payload. "I expect he was devastated, after so much hard work!" "No" said the American "Richard was delighted! He always used to say that you learned nothing from experiments that went exactly to plan. During the 9 seconds flight, the satellite was transmitting. Richard's team analysed the signals and realised they could redesign the system to make it 10 times more accurate." My companion explained that, if the original had flown, the Government would never have given the money for a more accurate replacement. That was one American's view of failure!

142. Japan looks to England...

In the late 1960s, Liverpool Polytechnic's Maritime Studies Department, particularly the radar research by Keith Jones's team started to attract interest from all over the world. Visitors came from as far afield as Japan, to see what we were doing. I showed a professor from Kobe University of the Mercantile Marine around the Department. When I described how we did things, I asked him how they taught the subject in Japan. At the end of the tour I said "I am surprised how similar our teaching is!" He said "Not surprising, really, we are using British Admiralty Manuals of Navigation!"

I said "Are there any questions you would like to ask?"

He said "I would like to make a short statement."

Bowing low, he said "In Japan we look to Engrand to take a lead in maritime affairs!"

I bowed low and replied "Thank you! We are honoured!"

Upon which he said "Why are you not doing so?"

Since that time, I think the UK has taken steps to use its maritime expertise more widely through organisations such as the International Maritime Organization and through companies involved in training, such as Videotel Marine International.

143. Japanese People are Very Polite

I was honoured to be asked to make a presentation on Maritime Training to the Japanese Shipowners' Association in Tokyo. Before the lecture, I was asked if I wanted

Japan, Cherry Blossom Time

an interpreter. Most of the audience spoke reasonable English, but, thinking of the question and answer session afterwards, I said yes, please. I delivered my lecture by showing pictures, speaking slowly and showing the text on the screen at the same time.

At the end of my presentation I asked my host "Was that alright?"

Very embarrassed, bowing and drawing breath in through his teeth, he said "Ooh! You are a very hard man!"

I said "I am sorry if I offended anyone!"

Him, "Japanese people are very polite and you are very hard!"

Me, "I am sorry!"

Him "Fortunately Japanese interpreter is a very polite lady, so they all think you are polite, but I know you are a very hard man!"

I had been surprised when I said something simple such as "The Rules will change in 2002" and the Japanese Lady spoke for about 5 minutes. She hedged all around the subject before delivering a message, which might upset the audience.

I was very grateful to her!

144. Semaphore

The UK research team looking at the manning of future ships was represented by Professor David Moreby of Plymouth in Japan. As well as visiting ship designers and builders, David visited shipowners. Many papers had been published about very advanced ships that could travel across the ocean unmanned, in fleets led by a "mother ship." The shipowners denied knowledge of these ships or plans to use them. "They are what our shipyards will build to sell to you!" They said.

Visiting Shimizu Seamens' School, David was surprised to see them still teaching signalling by semaphore. "We stopped teaching that years ago!" he said. A rather embarrassed college Principal said "We would like to stop, but we have no-redundancy agreement with lecturer and he unable to teach anything else!"

This was evidence of a Japanese culture in which companies took great pride in life-long care for their workers. It was to prove costly and make Japan uncompetitive against other new economies, where workers were less well treated.

145. Korean Culture

At a reception on board HQS Wellington, I met a lawyer who had a problem! Many collisions were being caused by young Korean Officers altering course to port, when they should have gone to starboard. They knew the source of the problem. It was a Professor at the Korean Maritime

Korean Maritime University

University who told the students "Starboard is better, but you can sometimes alter course to port!" He had omitted to tell them when. I asked why they did not just tell the Professor the problems he was causing. They said that, in Korean culture, University professors were so highly respected, that no-one dared tell them they had "got it wrong".

I was asked to go to Korea and give a lecture pointing out the error. They could then say to the professor "This very rude Englishman, who does not understand our customs, says you are giving poor advice to your students!"

The lecture hall in Busan held about 300 smart, uniformed students. The lecture was well received, but the first question was asked, and answered in Korean, by my host Videotel's agent Sam Park. I said "Do you want me to answer it?" Sam said no, but later told me "I gave you a big build up as being famous, having lectured all over the world. The girl's first question was "If he is that famous, why does he carry his own brief case?"

I had a lot to learn about Korean culture.

146. Chinese Philosophy

Our ship was loading in Singapore, and an old Chinese docker was doing a bit of fishing during his lunch break. He stood by the ship's rail, and at his feet were two small fish. He was smiling broadly and obviously very happy.

I said "Can you eat them?"

Him: "No, too small!"

Me: "Bad luck! But why are you so happy?"

Him "By catching small fish, I know that the ones still in the sea must be bigger, so I have improved my chances of catching a big one next time!"

He was content with his luck. A good example of Chinese philosophy.

147. Egypt during Ramadan

There must have been about 30 lecturers sitting round the table at the Arab Maritime Transport Academy in Egypt, listening to my presentation. At coffee time, coffee and biscuits were brought in just for me. It was the month of Ramadan and Islamic culture required the lecturers to fast from dawn until dusk. I felt uncomfortable and did not want to eat and drink in front of them.

My friend Commodore Ibrahim Hussein resolved the matter. He said "Our God requires us to fast. If we do, he gives us four stars. But if we watch you eating and drinking, he will give us five stars!"

Ibrahim was a resourceful and compassionate person.

148. Egyptians and Grass

A group of lecturers from Alexandria were in Liverpool on an up-dating course. The Department's minibus driver, Don, ferried them round and was told to be helpful to them. Don was very worried when one of the lecturers took him aside and whispered "Can you get me some 'grass'?" Don had not been expecting this and said: "You mean 'grass'?" Don made smoking gestures as if puffing marijuana. "No, no!" said the lecturer, "This sort of grass!" indicating lawn grass growing.

Egyptians grass would not grow under a shady tree at his home. Don got him some British grass seed to try.

149. Doctors of Philosophy

I never got as far as a PhD myself. I was going to, but Ann said "No". We had five children, One during study for First Mate, One for Master, Two for Extra Master (the

Exam had two parts, Part A and Part B) and One for my Master of Philosophy degree. Ann said we could not afford any more children!

Examining other people's PhDs, which I did for the University of Wales in Cardiff and for Plymouth Polytechnic, is hard work. I remember being dismayed when the postman staggered to my door with a very heavy thesis about 2.5 inches thick, from Cardiff. Later that day the University Registrar called to say "I have an apology to make. There has been a mistake. We meant to send you the thesis of William McMullen!" I said "You did send it, it arrived today!" "No, no!" He said "That was just Part A!" Part B was just as thick.

Normally a thick thesis means a lot of data, but very little thought, analysis or reasoning. Fortunately, not so in this case! The work was very well done and the data, mainly collected through William's students and former students at the United States Mercantile Marine Academy, was well used and remained for others to use in the future.

William still had to attend a Viva Voce examination. It started at about 9.30 am if I remember correctly and internal and external examiners peppered him with questions. By about 12.30 he was really exhausted. Told that he had passed, he confided that the questioning was so fierce that he thought he might fail. We said, "No chance! Your thesis was excellent and by 10 am we knew you had passed. We just wanted to explore the limits of your knowledge". A bit mean, perhaps, but a PhD is an achievement. They are not just "given away". He felt he had been well tested!

150. Bargaining

One of the first students from the Middle East who attended the BSc course, taught me a lesson about his culture.

About two weeks before the First Year Examinations, he came and asked me "How much for the questions?" I said we did not do that sort of thing and he apologised. About a week later he asked again and I was annoyed. He said "I am sorry, Sir, I have offended you! I will not mention it again!"

I was really angry when he asked for a third time. I took him into the staff room, sat him down and hammered the desk as I said "How many times do I have to tell you! We do not do that sort of thing here!...." He stopped me in mid-rant and said "One moment, Sir, I am sorry, I can't afford your price!" He thought we had been bargaining. Knowing now, that he was brought up to haggle over everything, and that everything had a price, I understand!

151. Malaysian Culture

The Malay expression "Tida Apa!" meaning "It does not matter", sums up their wonderfully relaxed attitude to life. We had several Malaysian degree students sponsored by their Government. One February day, a Malaysian student "disappeared" and we did not see him again until September, when he turned up to re-enrol.

Me: "Where have you been?"

Him: "Scotland!"

Me: "What do you mean, Scotland?"

Him: "Well. It was like this. It was February, and when I woke up it was raining. I looked at my timetable and saw that I had a double period of Marine Engineering that day. I did not like the lecturer very much. So I thought 'I know what I'll do. I have always wanted to visit Scotland. I will do that!' And I did, and now I am back"

Me: "Why did you come back now?"

Him: "The raspberry picking season has finished and I had seen what I wanted to see. I suppose I cannot be allowed to go into the Second Year?"

Me: "I am not sure that you should even be allowed to repeat the First Year. You wasted an opportunity that another student would have appreciated"

Him "Tida apa!"

He repeated the First Year.

152. Pakistan

As Nautical Institute President, I visited branches all over the world. I was made very welcome by the Pakistan Branch for a big dinner and conference in Karachi on World Maritime Day, one September. It took a while to adjust to the lifestyle – still with some reminiscences of the earlier days of the Raj.

Arriving tired after a long flight, I was taken to the Sindh Club where my first action was to undress and take a shower. When I came out of the shower, I thought my clothes had been stolen. They hadn't, it was just the dhobi wallah doing his job. Likewise one day I had a knock on my door and the shoe cleaner asked if my shoes needed cleaning. I had just cleaned them with a patent buffing pad. I said "No thank you!" About half an hour later, I was still in my room reading when there was another knock on the door "Shoes need cleaning yet, Sir?" I gave in.

Driving back from the very grand dinner, I was squeezed into a small car with my host and his wife and daughter. We were all big people. My host said "We are very proud that Pakistan now has its own car industry. Unfortunately the cars are designed in Japan and the Japanese are small people. We find that there is hardly enough room for our chauffeur!"

153. Is it French?

In 2006 we are having debates about Automatic Identification Systems for ships, which allow them to identify one another and communicate. Dr Keith Lindsay, researching at Liverpool Polytechnic had already had an insight into the answers more than 20 years before.

Under the supervision of Keith Jones, Keith Lindsay had programmed the new simulator to allow ships to get transponder-mediated information about the identity and characteristics of the other ships they saw on the radar. About six experienced shipmasters joined us for a week. On Monday Keith set up an exercise that included a ship carrying very hazardous cargo. He expected the other ships, now knowing this fact, to steer well clear of it. But they didn't – they treated it just the same as the rest. When asked, one old shipmaster replied "Look son, I don't want to collide with anything, so I treat them all the same!" Fair enough thought Keith. On Thursday afternoon the same shipmaster went way off his route to avoid another ship. Keith said "I thought you treated all ships the same?" "I normally do" he said, "But that one is French!"

154. Change of Orders

Keith Jones had invented a Collision Avoidance calculator, which told you how far you had to alter course and speed in order to avoid other ships by a certain distance. The BBC programme "Tomorrows World" came to Liverpool to interview Keith and film the device being used on the simulator, but then wanted to see it used in real life, in heavy traffic, so we went off to the English Channel and joined the British Rail ferry "Hengist". The presenter

William Woollard Tomorrow's World

179

impressed me. William Woollard memorised pages of script in minutes and delivered them, word perfect, as if they were his own words. We had a delay while a search was carried out for the helmsman's uniform cap. British Rail wanted its staff to appear properly dressed. So all the filming had to be done on the return trip.

As we approached Boulogne, the VHF radio crackled and a French voice said "'Ello Hengist! This is Boulogne Port Control, your berth is Number 35!" The Mate replied and then said to me "He has made a mistake, No. 35 is the small fishing boat berth next to ours. But I bet you he will not admit his mistake!"

We were almost through the breakwaters when the radio crackled again, "'Ello Hengist!" This is Boulogne Port Control, there 'as been a change of orders, your berth is Number 34!"

Not a mistake – a change of orders. Dignity had been preserved!

155. The Philippines

The 1990s saw me back in the Philippines, working with Videotel agent Kjell Sundberg, trying to implement traditional maritime training standards in a developing world economy. The Philippines supplied over 20% of the world's seafarers at that time.

I had recently been involved in making a training programme on "Search and Rescue". The UK Coastguard representative on the Videotel Steering Group in London came in from the rescue centre in Falmouth and told us about an event which had just happened. A ship had suffered an explosion, all the radios were destroyed and the only way they could get help was to climb over the side and paint a sign saying "Explosion. Three Dead. Help us". The sign worked and they were rescued. I was telling that story in a café in Manila, when a Filipino Manager said "That story is wrong. I was manager of that ship. I know what really happened!" I asked what was wrong with the story. He said, "It was not an explosion. It was a very intense fire!" Apart from that he confirmed the story. It is a small world.

On another visit to Manila, it was drummed into me that I must take the Hotel Limousine to the hotel, not an ordinary taxi, as there had recently been several kidnappings for ransom. On arrival, I carefully sought out the right limousine. The driver told me he had worked abroad in Saudi Arabia. His employers were cruel and he escaped and borrowed money for his flight home. I was sorry for him. As we approached the hotel he resumed his status as a driver. "Right, Sir!" he said "Now, first, have you got a room booked at the Hotel?"

Me: "Yes!"

Him: "And have you got a pretty girl booked for your room, Sir?"

Me: "No!"

Him: "I only asked because I know where to find one. But I see you have had a long flight, I understand! To help you relax before you go to sleep, I wonder if you would like to see a show with topless dancers?"

Me: "No, thank you!"

Him: "I understand, Sir, you are tired. I do not tell all my passengers, but for you, I know where to find a topless dancer who is topless all the way down. Would you like to see her?"

Me: "No, thank you"

Him (with a sigh): "I understand, Sir, you must be VERY tired!"

He must have thought "Some customers are very hard to please!"

156. Liverpudlians and Mancunians

I arrived at Liverpool Lime Street Station at 11 am one morning to be told that the London train was cancelled and we would have to go to Crewe to join a Manchester train. The sight of a train full of Liverpudlians joining their train did not please the Mancunians – who are a bit miserable anyway.

Shortly after the train got up to speed the door at the end of our carriage burst open and a voice with a trace of Liverpool accent said loudly "Tickets please!"

The settled Manchester lot felt in their pockets or got up to get their tickets from bags in the luggage rack. They were not happy. The lad walked the length of the carriage, turned round, smiled and said "Had you all going there, didn't I !!!" and left.

I later told this story to Jim Hitchmough (late author of the TV series "Watching") who had a wonderful Liverpool sense of humour. We agreed that would not have happened on a Liverpool train. Jim's comment was "No, on Liverpool trains that announcement would just result in all the toilets being very crowded!"

157. The Adelphi Hotel, Liverpool

I gave several after dinner speeches at the Adelphi Hotel in Liverpool. It was daunting, with several hundred guests and a not very good public address system.

On one occasion I had finished my speech and a Liverpool comedian was in full flow, when a door burst open and drunken nurses from a party in the next room, came dancing down the top table. Most Liverpool comedians would have really enjoyed the challenge, but this chap was thrown off his stride. Something had to be done. The Toastmaster, very calmly leaned over the shoulder of the host and whispered: "Do you want them in, Sir, or do you want them out?" The host (wistfully, because I think he was enjoying the show): "I suppose it had better be Out!"

On another occasion, I thought my speech had gone quite well, not too serious, with a few stories about students etc. In Liverpool a lot of the humour comes from Ireland or from the Irish community. They are very "laid back" in their attitude to life, but there is always good common sense in what they say.

I was surprised at the end of the meal, to be confronted by two very angry people. One, in the soft accent of Dublin said "I'm the representative from Dublin!" The other, in a hard Belfast accent, said "And I'm the representative from Belfast. Me and my friend are about bloody fed up with all your Irish jokes!"   I apologised, but thinking about it afterwards, I realised that I had done what others had tried to do and failed: I had united Ireland!

158. Boat Building

During my first week in Alexandria, I was invited to look round the City. One of the lecturers drove me round. The first object I asked questions about, was a memorial on the sea side of the coastal highway – the Corniche. We were in the fast lane of a very busy six-lane highway at the time, and as soon as I expressed an interest, my guide stopped the car and explained all about the memorial in great detail. We were stopped in the fast lane with cars swerving and screeching past. I do not remember much about his explanation!

In the fishing harbour, we stopped and watched Egyptian craftsmen making wooden boats. They were very skilled and took great care with their work, but the wood they were using was full of knots and cracks. I said "What a pity such skilled craftsmen do not have better material to work with!"   My guide told the boat builders what I had said. They replied and he translated for me "The Englishman is a fool! Even with this very poor wood, these boats last 20 years. If we used decent wood, they would last 100 years and we would be out of a job!"   Built-in obsolescence in an early form?

159. Learning the Right language

A few years ago, I was invited to provide some "updating" lectures for the Malaysian Maritime Academy in Malacca. I thought I had better brush up on my Malay Language, so went to the book shop at Liverpool University.

Me: "Have you got any books on the Malay Language?"

Young lady assistant; "I am not sure, Sir, but I can soon find out!"

A few minutes later she returned: "Sorry Sir, nothing on Malay, the nearest we have to it is Maltese!"

She certainly knew her alphabet, and I should have asked for Berhasa. We all live and learn.

160. Prince Henry the Navigator

The first nautical school in the world was the Escuela Infante Dom Henrique (The Prince Henry the Navigator School) founded in Sagres in Portugal. I was very pleased to be invited to lecture to students at the college, now located near Estoril, west of Lisbon.

I told them that they should be proud of their college, and I hoped that they would all grow up like Prince Henry.

Later, while being shown round the museum, my guide said "Do you know why the college was founded at Sagres (a remote town on the coast), rather than in Lisbon?" I said I did not. "Well" she said "When Prince Henry completed his exploration and came back to live in the King's Court, he embarrassed his father by bringing all his boy friends with him!"

I said "You mean girl friends!"

My guide: "Oh no, I don't"

I then thought back to the fact that my words in the morning at the college, "I hope you all grow up like him" had not been given a rousing reception.

When I went home, I told my history master, Mr Weaver, that he had only told me half the story, and had rather "dropped me in it". He smiled and said "Sorry!"

Out of the Mouths...

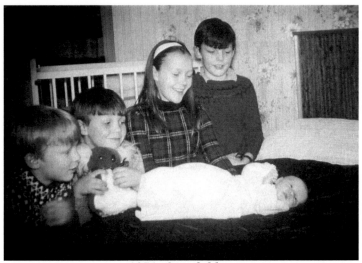

1971, Our children

161. Where Does Milk Come From?

Living in Liverpool and the Wirral, we were close to the hills of North Wales and enjoyed our car rides into the country. Having been brought up in rural Sussex during World War II, I knew quite a lot about country life and tried to explain things to the children. My efforts were not always successful.

I had pointed out milk lorries going round to the farms to collect churns of milk.

A very young Peter stored that information away, and the next time we saw a milk lorry calling at a farm he said "There is another lorry, taking milk to fill up the cows!" Nearly, but not quite right!

More recently daughter Alison asked me to grow vegetables in my garden at Towcester, so the grandchildren would not think that everything came from supermarkets. I let each of the grandchildren plant a potato and watch it grow. They were delighted to dig up several potatoes from the one they planted. They reported it as "news" at school. We had actually enlightened their Mum, Alison, too. She had thought seed potatoes just got bigger – she did not know they multiplied!

162. Meanness and Generosity

Ann's father had a reputation for being "tight" with his money, but in our generation, I am the "careful" one and Ann is very generous. I discovered our eldest son David, takes after me. He was away at Leicester University and each time he came home, he rang me up from Birkenhead Hamilton Square station and I went in the car, to collect him and bring him home. At some times of day, buses were not very frequent and he needed a lift. I discovered that he still rang for a lift, even when the bus was waiting opposite the station. "Why didn't you catch the bus?", I asked. He said "If I catch the bus, I pay the fare. If you collect me in the car, you buy the petrol!" It seemed perfectly logical to him!

163. Katherine's Enthusiasm

Whatever Katherine does, she throws herself into it with great enthusiasm. At Grammar School, at University and at work, this has resulted in considerable achievements, but when she was young, it nearly had dire consequences. While living in Liverpool, we used to take Katherine and

David to see the planes arriving and departing from Speke Airport. The children loved it, and from the first floor public balcony, waved enthusiastically to the passengers. Once, Katherine waved so enthusiastically that she toppled over the balcony rails! It was fortunate that there were window boxes on the outer edge of the balcony, so she finished up in one of those, rather than on the tarmac apron.

Later, we were feeding ducks at Raby Mere and Katherine, very competitive, tried to throw furthest, lost her balance and fell into the Mere. Of such stories are family archives built!

164. Peter's Independence

Youngest son Peter has always been "his own man." He makes his own mind up and does what he wants. When at junior school, he learned an important lesson. The first we knew about it was when Peter, breathless, rushed through the front door and up the stairs, shouting over his shoulder "You may have a visit soon, from a policeman!" Peter, young and innocent, had been playing with some young rascals who persuaded him to throw a brick through the window of a new house being built on a nearby estate. The boys then rang the police and reported the name and address of the criminal, Peter! I told the policeman I would take Peter round to see the foreman, and would make him pay for the damage out of his pocket money. The foreman wasn't bothered, he considered vandalism and theft of building materials a normal overhead and did not want the money, but I made him take it, to teach Peter a lesson. Peter now has a strong dislike of injustice, just like his mother.

As a young man, Peter had a job working for Colourvision, installing and repairing televisions. He came home one day saying the manageress had sacked him. I was annoyed when I discovered the reason. I sympathised with Peter and went to see the manageress. I said "I understand you send Peter out to repair the TVs of elderly people, when all he has to do is turn one control to get the picture back. You make him charge the full call-out fee of over £20. I agree with Peter, I think it is swindle!" She replied "The reason I sacked him, is that he called me a swindler in front of a shop full of customers" Peter got his job back.

He continues to be the most independent of our children.

165. Nick's Generosity

We worried about our children and motorbikes. We tried to get them "past" that stage and into cars where they had a bit more protection in accidents, but Peter and Nicholas like the freedom and economy of bikes.

A group of bikers were going down to South Wales one holiday morning. In the Welsh town of Chirk, Nick was "catching up" with the rest on his big bike, when he crossed a metal manhole cover, which was wet with dew. The back wheel traction went and the bike fell over, skidding down the road on its side, dragging Nick with the security chain he had round his chest, caught in the rear number plate. The bike went into the side of a MiniMetro coming the other way and put it out of commission. Remarkably, Nick suffered only shock, a scratch and few bruises, but no serious damage. He arrived home on a Recovery Vehicle. Nick's immediate thought was of other people. He said that he felt bad about spoiling the day out for the four youngsters in the Metro. He wanted to borrow my car to take them home to the Midlands. We did not think he was fit to drive, so David in his car, and me in ours, "rescued" the stranded group and took them home. Their parents seemed surprised that the Holder family had done that, but that is how we are!

166. Baby Alison and The Lady Doctor

With her rheumatoid arthritis, Alison, even when very young, had met a lot of male doctors and consultants. When she was due for her normal "assessment" for basic faculties and development, she met her first female doctor. During the assessment, Ann had to tell the doctor all the things she could say and do, and Alison just looked at the doctor and said and did nothing. When outside she asked her mum "Do some doctors look like women?" She expected all doctors to be men and could not understand why this one was wearing a dress!

167. Feminine Logic or Her Father's Daughter?

Our eldest daughter borrowed the family car to visit her boyfriend on a farm in Wales. Shortly after she returned I noticed the car aerial was missing. I asked "What happened to the aerial?" She replied, "I am sorry, but it was not my fault. The farmer planted his hedge in the wrong place".

Footnote: To be fair to Katherine, I think the farm track had very deep wheel ruts which went close to the hedge and the car had steered itself into it.

168. Polite Society

Our Grandchildren, 2002

It is not easy to teach children to be polite and say "Please" and "Thank you" in a world where so many people are rude and aggressive.

Amy: "Mummy, I want a biscuit!"

Mummy: "Amy, haven't you forgotten a little word?"

Amy: "Oh yes! Mummy, I want a biscuit", jabbing a finger at the floor "NOW!!!"

169. Why do people learn a language?

With children who think about things a "penny dropping" sometimes reveals a strange logic. Katherine was very young when the school decided it would be a good idea to teach the basic rudiments of foreign languages at primary school. It was a new idea, and it puzzled her for a while, until she joyfully told us "I know why people learn French, German and Mathematics at school! It is so that you can speak the language when you go to the countries!"

At the time, I thought that including Mathematics in this list was a mistake on her part. However, since working with German Engineers in Brussels and Naval Architects all over the world, I have learned that they usually "speak in mathematics" and if you do not speak it, you will feel lost if you try to go there.

170. The Last Drop

We had two teenage sons living at home, unable to find work during a difficult time in the early 1980s. They had both passed their driving tests, and I used to go into work on the bus, so the car was at home. I discovered that I would leave the petrol tank full, and next time, find it empty, so a battle of wits developed. I used to leave the car nearly empty. They would leave it <u>really</u> empty. Being compassionate lads and not wishing to embarrass us, they sometimes said "Don't try to fill the car at the garage up the hill, Dad, it may not make it! Safer to go down the hill" (Their Mum would find it easier to push!)

171. Job Prospects

On a rainy bank holiday the grandchildren were getting bored and I offered to take them down to the banks of the River Mersey to see the ships. On the way back, there was a very interesting discussion on the back seat of the car, between Peter's Amber (aged about 6) and Alison's Daniel (about 5 years old).

Amber: "What do you want to do when you grow up, Daniel?"

Daniel: "I don't know, I haven't really thought about it!"

Amber (shocked): "You mean to say, you have reached the aged of 5 and you have NO IDEA what you want to be when you grow up! I am amazed!"

172. Tom Kitten

Reading bedtime stories is a time when you really get to know your children and grandchildren. I know the Beatrix Potter stories, Jemima Puddleduck, The Tale of Two Bad Mice, Squirrel Nutkin, Peter Rabbit etc, off by heart. My parents read them to me. I read the tale of Tom Kitten to Daniel. Briefly, Tom is scrubbed up and put in his best clothes, and sent into the garden while Mrs Cat gets ready for visitors. Tom bursts the buttons on his coat, loses it over the garden wall and some passing ducks find it, put it on, and lose it in the pond. Mrs Cat then spanks Tom Kitten and sends him to bed. I finished the story, and Dan fell asleep.

At breakfast Dan said, "Grandad, I've been thinking about Tom Kitten. It was not his fault. The Puddleducks lost the jacket, so Mrs Cat should not have spanked Tom!" I said he could well be right!. At lunch he said "I've done some more thinking. I don't think it was the Puddleducks' fault! It was really Mrs Cat's own fault, she did not sew the buttons on properly in the first place!"

Daniel is a very thoughtful and intelligent young man and very interesting to talk to!

173. Ladies and Handbags

Ladies and their handbags have a relationship, which mere males do not understand.   On a long journey, we were in a Little Chef Café after having a meal. Teenage grandson Steven observed Ann pick up her handbag and go to the "Ladies". Steven tried to work out what was going on.

He asked:

"Grandad, why does Grandma always take her handbag to the toilet with her? Doesn't she trust us? Maybe he had solved the mystery!"

174. You can tell from the eyes

These days, lots of farms are open to the public and welcome visitors to see the farmers and shepherds at work.   Lambing is a busy time in the Northamptonshire countryside. We took Daniel and Amy to see the young lambs. Daniel said, "Grandma, are all the lambs girls? "No, some are girls and some are boys," she said. We waited with baited breath when Dan said "I think I know how you can tell the difference!" We waited for a lecture on the anatomy of rams and ewes and were really quite relieved when he said, "You can tell by looking into their eyes!"

Shortly after that time, my sister Elizabeth was explaining to Dan, that her great granddaughter Michelle was soon going to have a baby.

Elizabeth said, "So you will soon have a new cousin, but we don't know yet if it will be a boy or a girl."

Dan said "I think I can help you there! It all depends on what goes on down there, (pointing downwards), If it has a Willy it's a boy. If it hasn't, it is a girl!" Elizabeth thanked him for his advice!

175. Cinderella

In these days of Gay Liberation and political correctness, the traditional pantomime, in which the dames are men and the principal boy is a girl, children are bound to be confused. Modern children are also encouraged to be out-going and confident, so in the middle of the pantomime, when Cinderella was about to marry the Prince, one of Daniel's party stood up and shouted "You can't marry that one, its a girl!" To hell with political correctness!

176. Points of View

On Saturday, Ann and I with grandson Daniel (aged 9) watched the excellent reconstruction of the "Herald of Free Enterprise" tragedy on the National Geographic TV Channel. The accident worried Dan a bit, but I explained that steps had been taken to make sure it never happens again, and he told me about the closed-circuit TV and special light signals which he had noticed in the programme.

On Sunday morning I showed Dan two Videotel Bridge Resource Management dramatised Case Studies and explained how we use them to teach people to learn from mistakes and not repeat them.

Dan: "Did you make those videos?"

Me: "Yes, we make them"

Dan: "That's really great! I knew you had something to do with ships. I thought you cleaned them, I didn't know you stopped them having accidents"

Now he knows. I have been raised a bit in his estimation.

Where did the "cleaning" bit come from? Pictures of me as a cadet with a bucket or paintbrush, I suppose.

Washing the funnel

177. It is not my fault!

In 2000 we had a visit from Katherine and her teenage daughter Sandra, and Peter's family, with young daughters Amber and Ceri.

Sandra asked Ceri "How old are you?"

Ceri replied: "3"

Sandra corrected her: "No, you are not, you are two and a half!"

Ceri said : "Well, it is not my fault!"

178.   Some Things Change, Some Stay The Same

Having been asked to look after the grandchildren on a wet afternoon, I decided to show them some old family photographs. They always like to see their parents, uncles and aunts as children. I showed them a picture of myself at 21 and said "Who is that?" Daniel replied "It's you Granddad. You are very easy to recognise. Your smile has not changed a bit". A nice thought, that my smile has not changed in 48 years, but we all know the rest of me is a bit more wrinkly and faded.

Daniel